Logic Analyzers for Microprocessors

Logic Analyzers for Microprocessors

JOHN KNEEN

Professor of Electrical Engineering
Royal Melbourne Institute of Technology
Consulting Engineer, Hewlett-Packard Co.

Edited by Charles H. House

Logic Analyzers Operations Manager, Hewlett-Packard Co.

HAYDEN BOOK COMPANY, INC.
Rochelle Park, New Jersey

Library of Congress Cataloging in Publication Data

Kneen, John.
Logic analyzers for microprocessors.

Includes index.
1. Logic circuits. 2. Automatic checkout equipment.
3. Microprocessors—Testing. I. House, Charles H. II. Title.
TK7868.L6K54 621.3819'5835 80-18615
ISBN 0-8104-0953-4

Printed in the United States of America

1 2 3 4 5 6 7 8 9 PRINTING

80 81 82 83 84 85 86 87 88 YEAR

Editor's Preface

The logic analyzer concepts described in this book represent the latest step in the evolution of a new breed of diagnostic test equipment for digital system troubleshooting.

The way in which these instruments have evolved is very interesting, and the implications are widespread for many engineers, technicians, and even company managements. This much is clear: the world of electronics is on the threshold of a profound revolution in the nature of design tasks and diagnostic requirements, not to mention the opportunities and challenges in new product development.

The nature of these changes may be illustrated by considering the interplay among component suppliers, end-product manufacturers, users, and test equipment suppliers.

For all of these groups, the classical analysis techniques seemed appropriate in the 1960s. Those techniques, as we all know, were the frequency domain and time domain approaches pioneered by the mathematics of Maxwell, Fourier, Heaviside, and LaPlace. Voltmeters, oscilloscopes, counters, and spectrum analyzers are but a few of the many test instruments that have evolved to facilitate analysis by these techniques. Significantly, these instruments were basically the same whether used in a lab, production, or field-service environment—differing, to be sure, in portability, cost, accuracy, and sophistication, but not in terms of the parametric test method.

The advent of integrated circuits and minicomputers led to a significant expansion of computer-based system design opportunities, and eventually to a modification of the product design cycle. The major difference to note is the addition of a "systems-design" block to the components-to-user-chain, an admission of the importance of applications software design, I/O considerations, and support peripherals. Note that these designers were not very often designing hardware, except for translators, buffers, and other circuits needed to overcome a basic interface mismatch between two system parts. Designers and troubleshooters frequently found themselves spending long hours debugging software, searching for glitches, or checking for noise margins. To ease their problems, they resorted to using one minicomputer to develop another—in-house groups built simulators, and even assemblers and editors, to help them develop applications software more quickly. For field service, diagnostic routines became embedded in the software.

In effect, a new class of instrumentation was being defined as a function of need. This need was almost transparent to the outside world, because in large part electronic engineers not at a minicomputer company were still designing circuits on a nodal basis, and test equipment used by designers and computer service technicians still included voltmeters, counters, and scopes. In fact, scopes were still the primary digital troubleshooting tools after the diagnostic routine indicated that a problem existed.

But such inefficient tools! The errors in computers are largely errors of signal data flow. A flag line fails to set at the right time, the memory address is read incorrectly, the wrong instruction is executed, the data being massaged is transmitted with a dropped bit—these are not electrical parameter failures, except that they are incidentally accomplished with electronic circuits. They are data errors, occurring because of an incorrect data sequence, and as such their analysis is more appropriately considered data domain analysis.

INTO THE DATA DOMAIN

The characterization of data domain analysis concepts evolved during the late 1960s, based on a conviction that classical test instruments were largely irrelevant to the design and test requirements of the rapidly growing computer industry. That view was partially shaped by Hewlett-Packard's design experience with desk-top computers, hand-held calculators, and minicomputer controller systems.

Nodal testers were the earliest aids for design and troubleshooting of digital systems, and they are still the least expensive. By the early 1970s, logic probes, clips, comparators, current tracers, and totalizing counters had become widely used to locate stuck nodes, pulse activity, shorts and opens, and pulse burst counts. The time-space information content of digital signals is so important, however, that these simple tools have been augmented by more precise techniques based upon error-correcting code theory.

Perhaps the most powerful way of compressing large amounts of data is typified by the classical cyclic redundancy checksum (CRC) generated for error checking in large memory systems. "Signature analysis" techniques based upon CRC patterns are now appearing in instruments for data comparison analysis where large amounts of data must be monitored, collated, and analyzed in a short time by an unskilled operator. The technique requires some interactive work by the digital system designer to provide the proper signal checks and buffers from extraneous phenomena (such as electromechanical switch bounce), but the serviceability and analysis power of the technique usually far outweigh the initial design investment.

Logic analyzers were first conceived as "digital scopes," which for clarity were scope-like tools in terms of value for digital designers, rather than digitizing scopes. The work began with a duality, describing a function of word and event, f(W,E), analogous to the time domain function of volts and time, f(V,t). This allowed development of trigger word conditions that were also analogous to scope functions.

Sampled data was also viewed in a different context—sampling theory had always been used to develop a stroboscopic reconstruction of continuous high-frequency phenomena. The mathematics of state variables and algorithmic-state-machine (ASM) concepts became very popular topics in the early 1970s, and state-flow data table presentations are a clear outgrowth of this work. Thus, sampled-data theory moved from a relation with time-domain analysis on continuous phenomena to data-domain analysis on discontinuous or truly discrete event-time phenomena.

An important consideration is the total amount of data that must be collected at every event-time in order to characterize system behavior. The program counter, the instruction register, the accumulators, and so forth, contain specific coded data that collectively describe the machine status at any one event-time. In addition, most digital machines are built to operate on external data—to add, subtract, multiply, or divide data, to make branching decisions from data comparisons, and to accumulate, store, and process still more data. Thus, to select data domain analysis as a descriptor for a way of analyzing digital logic machines suggests both an awareness of the machine's external function of working with digital data and its internal operation in terms of an organized flow of data sequences.

Data domain analysis, then, is a set of analysis techniques concerned with designing, monitoring, and correcting the behavior of a digital machine as a function of its internal data sequences and its external data manipulations.

LOCATING THE PROBLEM

Data domain problems are manifested as improper data sequences. It is important to note that the problem effect is always functional (i.e., data errors are transmitted) whether the cause is functional or electrical. This is true even for noise or voltage margin testing. Consequently, the first analysis step is locating the malfunction in the data flow sequence.

Locating a problem in data flow with an external instrument requires data registration or synchronization between the two systems, followed by data capture, possible manipulation, and presentation to the user. To meet these needs, Hewlett-Packard introduced in 1973 two logic state analyzers—one for parallel data words, the second for serial, while Biomation introduced a parallel word logic timing analyzer. The instruments were very modest in capability, but they caused much excitement for the concept and its application to the "computer-on-a-chip" revolution that was being born in 1973.

TODAY'S EQUIPMENT

After several years of experience now, some obvious subtrends have emerged within this instrumentation area. We may differentiate among three major groups of equipment: development aids, bus analyzers, and nodal testers. We have already mentioned nodal testers. Logic state and timing analyzers are bus analyzers. Development aids are tools aimed at improving the time-efficiency of digital design, primarily in software and IC development. In today's equipment, they frequently contain embedded logic analyzers. This book concentrates primarily on logic analyzers.

SYSTEM BUS ANALYZERS

The nodal testers are of chief value when it is known that a particular product or module is malfunctioning. Bus analyzers are of value for the more difficult task of ascertaining which portion of a system is malfunctioning. For example, a full system may have a central single-board computer, two disk memory units, two data-entry terminals, and twenty on-line process-control transducers. We may fully expect the four peripheral units to incorporate one or more microprocessors themselves, resulting in a multicomputer network of sorts. Unraveling the network transactions is the first priority for troubleshooting.

We may characterize each major bus area as CPU, I/O, and peripheral. The relevant parameters of the CPU bus structure are synchronous with clock speeds, usually 3 MHz or less (for virtually all minicomputer and microprocessor systems). Bus contents may be address, data, instructions, and control signals. The I/O bus, in contrast, usually carries asynchronous, multiplexed data at speeds up to 10 MHz. Moreover, it sometimes runs much longer physical distances in a facility. Consequently, we may expect to find that race conditions, noise spikes, and glitches from various causes are much more significant problems on an I/O bus than on a CPU bus. Moreover if they exist, they will be much harder to trace to a source because of the multiplexed architecture and data flow at a particular point.

The CPU and I/O buses generally are parallel buses, which means, among other things, that the data format may be the same on both. Peripheral buses, in contrast, usually employ serial data transmission, which requires further data formatting. They are lengthy buses, but with very slow data rates, so glitches are not so significant except in batch transmissions (e.g., across the continent).

The point to be recognized here is that designing, installing, and servicing a general computer network is not a trivial task for which a simple tester can be described. At the same time, some very usable general-purpose testers that will work in a variety of these application areas can be defined.

The current second-generation set of logic analyzers described in this book are configured for most bus analysis problems more or less on a bus-by-bus basis, with the very significant inclusions of cross-bus event correlation and very powerful selective data trace for linked and nested loop algorithms.

John Kneen's energy, enthusiasm, and dedication in the early years of logic analyzers development were important in introducing the concepts of these powerful design and analysis aids to potential users and instructors alike.

After working with these equipments at the Royal Melbourne Institute of Technology and with Australia's IEEE group, John initiated a sabbatical year with Hewlett-Packard in Colorado Springs, where we came to know and value his insight and approach to describing these techniques. He was particularly instrumental, along with Bruce Farly, in organizing and conducting the initial portions of the "Hewlett-Packard University Associates Program." This program involved professors from more than fifty universities, with the intent of developing understanding of these tools as an adjunct to modern digital design methodology.

This book is an outgrowth of those efforts, and as such represents a valuable contribution for the beginning designer, for the working engineer who is now considering microcontrollers for his area of major expertise, and for the student. John and many of us at Hewlett-Packard, however, see the book as being dedicated to laboratory instructors everywhere who share deep concerns for the available time and understanding permitted for student development by our increasingly pressured society. I think that this book will help to create understanding as well as serve as a useful later reference without requiring significant learning time.

WHERE IS THE FUTURE?

The original data-domain thesis is, of course, but a beginning. It is important that we recognize that the breadth of the data-domain analysis embraces not only local transactions of word-events, but the entire global picture of data state-space usage. This, consequently, includes the statistical pattern of event-flows (e.g., histograms, repetitive CRC sums, or perhaps even correlation for ergodicity), and it suggests that the mathematics of data-domain analysis already exists, but is not recognized conjunctively yet with these measurement techniques.

As we move into the 1980s, data-domain analysis equipment will become all-pervasive in our industry. Very-large-scale integrated circuitry (VLSI) and its extensions offer not only the opportunity for lower-cost, higher-performance products for our society but also the opportunity to change our design and test philosophies. What data-domain analysis tools make possible is top-down design for digital designers—which should permit us to consider not only block-structured programming languages, but block-structured IC layout and block-structured diagnostic and test routines. Without this change, we could imagine the fast-paced semiconductor revolution producing a chip capability of one million junctions or more for perhaps $10 by 1985—and then finding that IC designers or software designers need two or more years to use the $10 device.

The tools described in this book, along with their extensions in data-domain analysis techniques, will help the electronics revolution from VLSI continue.

Charles H. House

Colorado Springs
Colorado

Contents

Logic Analyzers for Microprocessors

CHAPTER ONE

Digital System Measurements

1.1 INTRODUCTION

Most modern digital systems are processor based. Initially, multi-device circuits were developed within the one chip to take advantage of the increased reliability possible with modern IC construction techniques. The microprocessor is a natural consequence of this trend and has additional advantages. The tremendous power of the microprocessor allows it to perform many tasks; the need for a large inventory of different components to perform dedicated tasks is eliminated. In addition, since the microprocessor is software controlled, the system function may be readily changed without the need for expensive hardware modifications. However, the microprocessor system creates its own problems, one of which is monitoring and analyzing system operation. It is this problem that will be addressed.

1.2 PROCESSOR BASED SYSTEMS

The majority of modern digital systems that are processor based are represented by the block diagram in Fig. 1-1. Even this simple system may have 28 lines (16 address, 8 data, 4 control) that should be monitored to obtain a complete description of internal system operation. Should the I/O ports require observation, the requirements on the monitoring instrument are increased.

The three buses of the processor system have different features, and that ultimately requires different functions in monitoring instruments. The address and data bus carry information that is synchronous with one or more of the control lines or clocks. The information occurring on these buses is relevant only about the active edge of the appropriate clock. For the control lines and parallel I/O lines, the time sequence in which various lines change state is important. On a serial data port or bus, both the word and framing are of consequence.

The digital system life cycle is diagrammed in Fig. 1-2. Once the design is defined, development proceeds along two paths. The software team

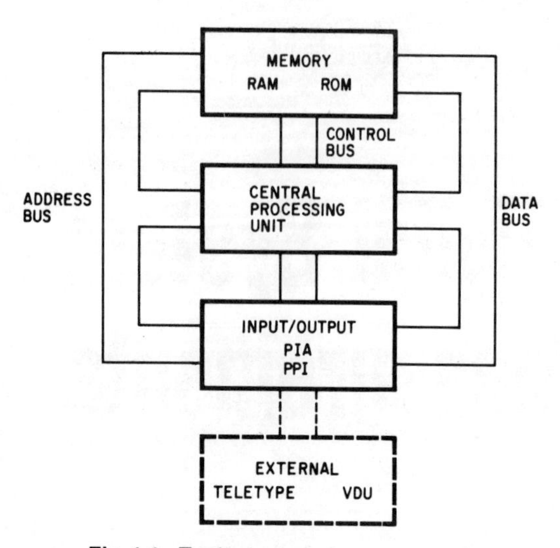

Fig. 1-1. Typical microprocessor system.

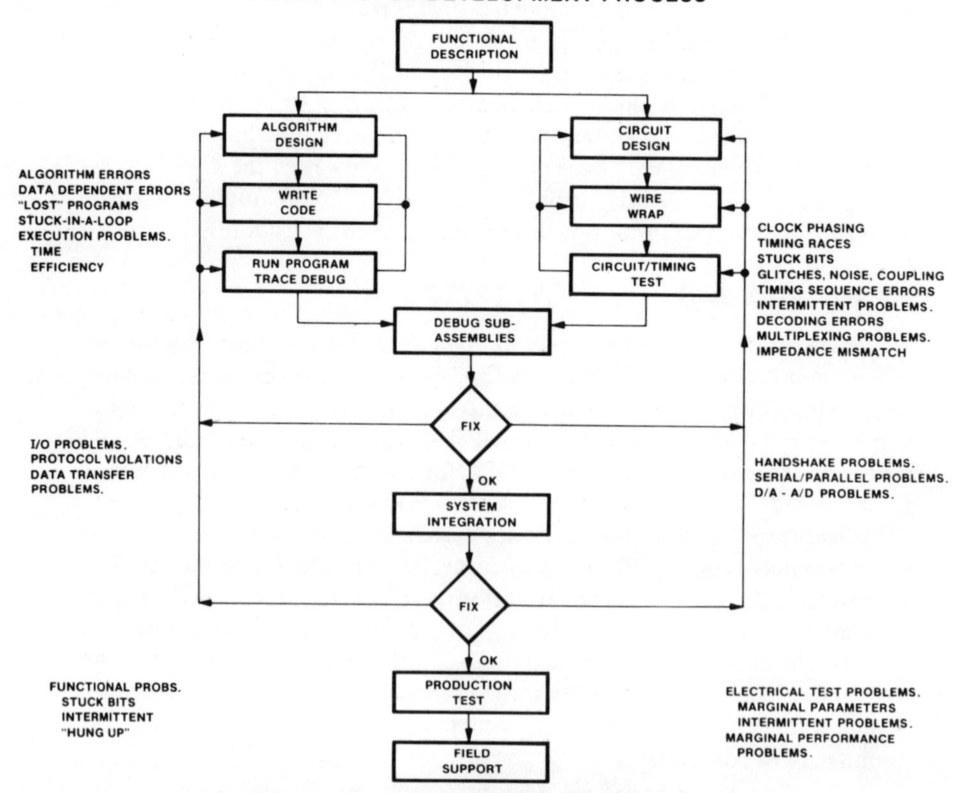

Fig. 1-2. Digital system development process.

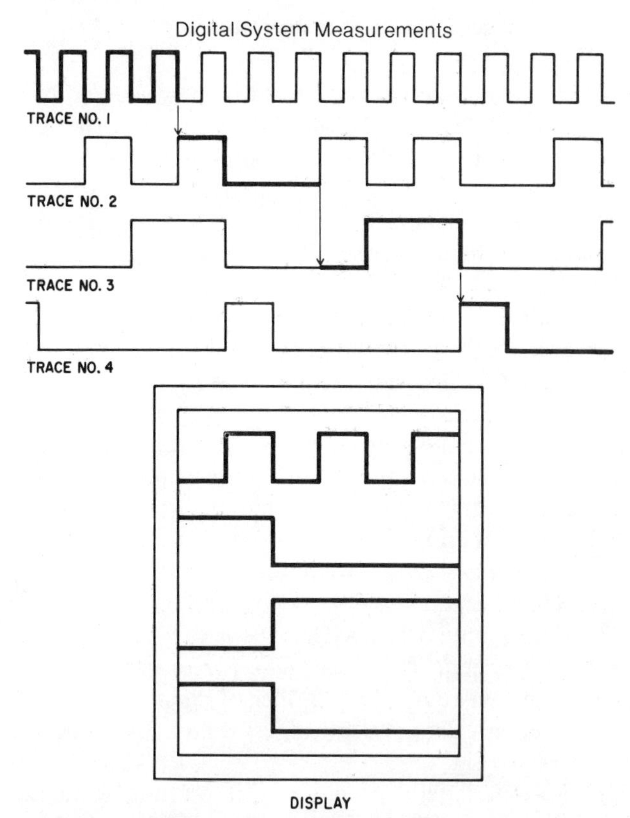

Fig. 1-3. Oscilloscope waveforms with the oscilloscope in the alternate mode. Unless special trigger circuits are used and the signals are repetitive, the waveforms on screen will not be synchronized.

concentrates on generating code, while the hardware team develops memory and interface devices. Eventually, the two paths must come together for final development. Once design is satisfactorily tested, production follows, and finally, service. At different phases in system development, different monitoring functions are needed. For the development stage, the monitoring instrument capabilities must be relatively sophisticated; at the production stage, many high speed tests are important. In field service, portability and ease-of-use are the dominant needs. The effects of these measurement requirement criteria are discussed in the following sections.

1.3 LIMITATIONS OF OSCILLOSCOPES

Until recently, the conventional instruments for testing equipment were the multimeter for steady conditions and the oscilloscope for variant or time dependent signals. Oscilloscopes are ideal instruments for displaying voltage information—such as rise and fall times, ringing, overshoot, or pulse width of a signal channel or node. However, modern digital systems contain many nodes that should be viewed simultaneously. Very few oscilloscopes displayed more than two channels of data. In monitoring bus activity, an operator chose one channel as a reference and monitored each of the other lines in turn. While unsatisfactory, for many years this was the only technique available.

One solution would be the development of an oscilloscope with many channels. However, such an oscilloscope would have some fundamental limitations. *Operated in alternate mode,* it would be essential that the system under test be repetitive and provide a trigger signal to synchronize all the waveforms on the oscilloscope display. This trigger problem was recognized by early manufacturers of digital troubleshooting equipment who marketed instruments for digital word pattern recognition. Figure 1-3 shows a signal that is not correctly synchronized. The display shows the hexadecimal sequence AB4545 when it should have showed the decimal sequence 0, 1, 2, 3, . . . *In the chop mode,* an oscilloscope has a maximum chop frequency (f) of only a few MHz, about the same as the clock frequency of a typical system under test. The performance falls short by a factor of at least 2n, where n is the number of channels. With the oscilloscope in chop mode, only data at a rate of less than f/2n can be ''faithfully'' reproduced on screen. (Fig. 1-4.)

The equipment designer needed to return to fundamentals and ask exactly what information was required to successfully monitor a digital system. This will be discussed in the following sections.

1.4 NECESSARY DIGITAL SYSTEM MEASUREMENTS

Functional Measurements

Let us consider a microprocessor development kit. Frequently, these kits offer the capability to single step the system. Internal circuitry, possibly only LEDs on the address and data buses, indicates the information passing across these lines on each clock cycle. Given a knowledge of the microprocessor instructions, an operator could decode the information and determine what is happening in the system and whether it is operating as expected.

For example, consider latching the address, data, R/W, and synchronization lines on a 6502 microprocessor system and stepping through four clock cycles. Suppose the results are

R/W	Syn	Address	Data
1	1	0202	8D
1	0	0203	01
1	0	0204	17
0	0	1701	20

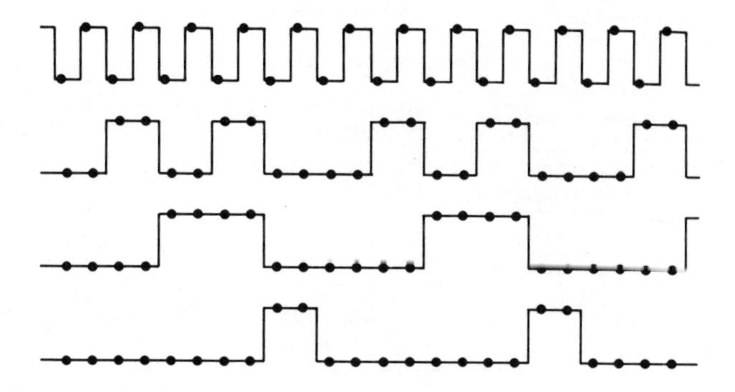

Fig. 1-4. Oscilloscope waveforms for signals in the chop mode. The maximum data rate has been assumed to be eight times the chop frequency.

where the address and data lines have been converted to hexadecimal. These four listings could be interpreted as follows:

(a) From the address 0202, read the op code for the next instruction. (8D = store accumulator)
(b) From the two succeeding locations, read the address in which the accumulator is to be stored. (1701)
(c) Execute the instruction found; i.e., store the accumulator (20) in location 1701.

By observing all these pieces of information, the operator can verify that both hardware and software are executing as intended. In this manner, system verification is achieved by knowing

(a) the state on each clock pulse
(b) the sequence of states

On synchronous systems, such as the address and data buses of a microprocessor, the information required is the state and state-sequence at each active clock edge. It is sufficient that the operator knows whether the voltage levels are above or below the threshold voltage of the system under test. For asynchronous buses, such as the control lines of a microprocessor system or the I/O lines, the operator needs to know in what sequence the various signal lines changed state and how long each signal was in a given state. The state-time relationship is important, not the voltage time. These measurements are functional measurements. A complete functional analysis indicates the state of the system at given discrete intervals in time, and the time at which the signals changed shape.

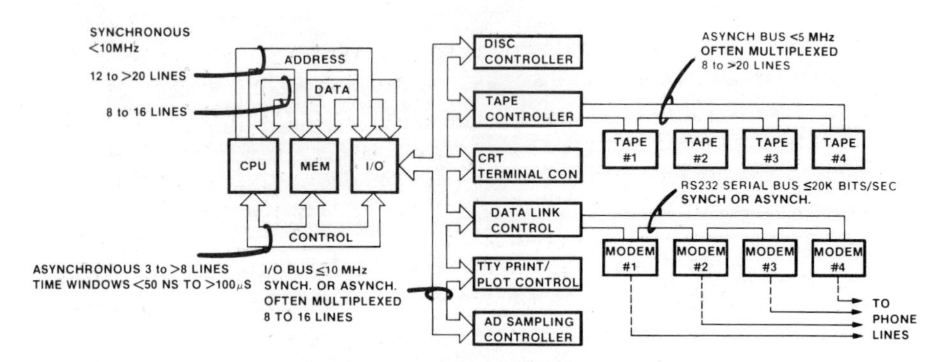

Fig. 1-5. Typical digital system bus structure.

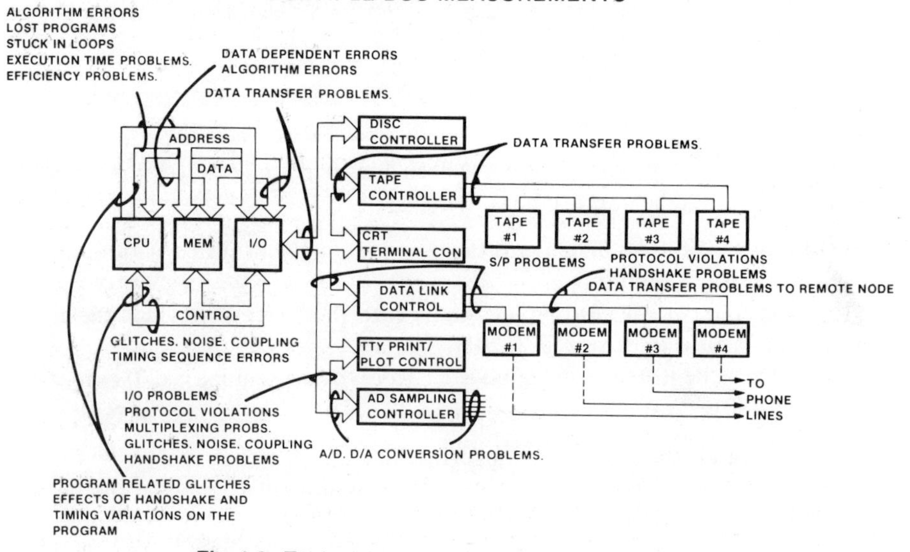

Fig. 1-6. Typical digital system and problem areas.

Measurement Capability Required

To study the functional measurements in more detail, see Figs. 1-5 and 1-6 for sample architecture of a digital system and common problems to be considered.

The first type of measurement that may be made on such a system involves tracing the state flow, that is, the sequence in which the various logic states occur. This technique identifies and solves the problems of Group 1 in Fig. 1-6. State flow tracing implies connection to at least the address bus, and preferably to the data bus as well, in order to simultaneously monitor and correlate address and data bus activity. These buses are typically synchronous parallel with a total of 20 to 40 lines operating at less than 10 MHz. Since the information on these buses may be multiplexed, some form of qualification will be necessary in the measurement. Other measurements related to Group 1 problems are time interval measurements between selected states to verify the timing of wait loops and strobe pulses.

Given the capability of monitoring the address and data bus, the next important criteria for any monitor instrument is the ability to window its display to the desired word or sequence of words or events. Any adequate monitor instrument must have extensive triggering capability.

The second group of measurements is related to problems encountered on the control bus and the effect of these problems on the program execution of the system. Basic measurements are time intervals and sequences of events. The monitor instrument must have the capability to highlight timing sequences and glitches and to reference the display to conditions that occur for specified time durations and to specified glitches. These measurements become even more meaningful when correlated to activity on either the address or data bus.

Problems listed in Group 3 are related to data transfer—either from the processor data bus to the I/O bus or port, or from the I/O bus to a peripheral device. Various I/O buses of a digital system use many different formats depending on the type of peripheral devices that are present. Serial communication, whether synchronous or asynchronous, is common. The IEEE-488 instrumentation interface bus has additional requirements because the data is transmitted in parallel but the three handshake lines change asynchronously. Simple tracing techniques are sufficient to monitor these lines, but the information is more meaningful when correlated to data or program flow on one of the other buses.

The following chapters will address the logic state analyzer and logic timing analyzer along with any preprocessing necessary to show how these instruments attack the digital measurement problems highlighted in Figs. 1-5 and 1-6. One important attribute of a logic analyzer, whether state or timing, is the ability to trap or trace data preceding the occurrence of a trigger condition, thus allowing observation of conditions that led to the problem. This negative time capability is a feature that cannot be provided by an oscilloscope.

CHAPTER TWO

Logic State Analyzers

2.1 INTRODUCTION

The traditional troubleshooting tool, the oscilloscope, will not handle the multinodal or multichannel monitoring requirements of modern digital systems. To monitor state and state-sequence in a digital system, the oscilloscope has been replaced by a logic state analyzer. Following is a discussion of some of the capabilities and design criteria of the logic state analyzer. As previously noted, the first important criteria is that a logic state analyzer be multichannel. A minimum number of channels for monitoring simple microprocessor-based systems is 24, 16 address lines and 8 data lines. More advanced systems use the 16-bit processors that require $\geq$32 channels for monitoring. A full computer could use over 100 monitoring channels.

The logic state analyzer monitors the digital system under test and displays state and sequence flow. In principle, the state-sequence could be captured using a bank of shift register memories. If sampled synchronously with the clock of the system under test, data could be clocked into the memory. Once the clock is removed, the state-sequence would be frozen in the registers and displayed as the analyzer's measurement.

The input circuit of the logic state analyzer, shown as a sampler in Fig. 2-1, interprets the logic state. Therefore, it must have the same logic characteristics as the system under test. When a variety of logic families is to be monitored, the operator must be able to adjust the logic threshold level to that of the system under test.

2.2 DISPLAYS

Binary List or Table

In a simple, self-contained logic state analyzer, the contents of the analyzer memory could be displayed using a bank of LEDs, either word-by-word or several words at a time. Alternatively, the memory data may be used to construct a pseudo state-time display on an oscilloscope. With either

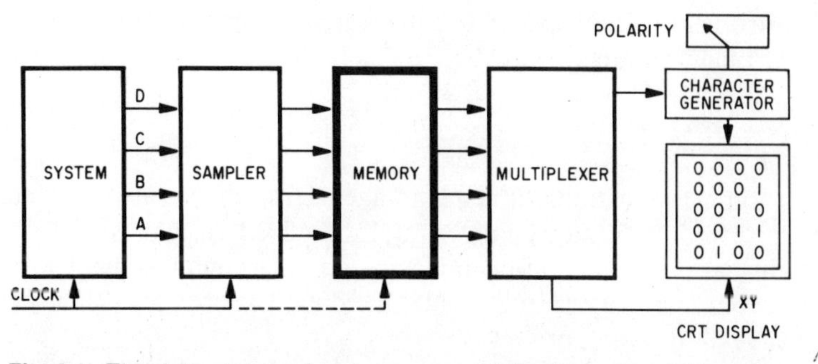

Fig. 2-1. The data state and sequence are latched into the shift register memory, word-by-word. The output circuitry takes the memory contents bit-by-bit and displays them as a list of 1's and 0's, depending upon the data and logic polarity chosen. In this example, the state is displayed horizontally (DCBA), while the sequence is shown vertically from top to bottom.

presentation, the results should be put into a more functional form. In digital systems, one functional presentation is the list or table, which corresponds closely to the program listing. The circuitry to generate the list or table is shown in Fig. 2-1. Each memory bit or location in turn would be tested by the multiplexer unit, and the appropriate "1" or "0" sent to the display. Additional controls might include (1) *logic polarity control* to permit a choice of positive or negative logic, (2) *shift control* (CRT display dimensions are limited) to provide shifting or memory roll to view the required portion of the trace on the display, and (3) *word width control* to define word width when formatting the analyzer.

The CRT display of Fig. 2-2 is called a list or table, and it provides the operator with a very detailed presentation of the state and sequence flow. Each horizontal line presents one word or state of the system under test. Vertically, the display shows the sequence of states in discrete instances in time (DIT) or time events. If data is sampled on every clock pulse and the clock is constant in frequency, the time intervals will also be constant. However, in practice this need not be so.

Formatted Lists

Binary results, the language of a digital machine, are cumbersome and subject to reading errors. To facilitate interpretation, the binary display may be formatted into groups of three or four bits. Taken one step further, the groups may be displayed as either an octal or hexadecimal equivalent. For example,

in octal: 1010010111001100 = 1 010 010 111 001 100
$= 122714_8$

in hexadecimal: 1010010111001100 = 1010 0101 1100 1100
$= \text{A5CC}_{16}$

Some instruments also display a decimal format. The decimal equivalent of the above binary number would be

$2^{15} + 2^{13} + 2^{10} + 2^{8} + 2^{7} + 2^{6} + 2^{3} + 2^{2}$
$= 32768 + 8192 + 1024 + 256 + 128 + 64 + 8 + 4$
$= 42{,}444_{10}$

In some applications, it is advantageous to define various groups of inputs in different formats. For example, a mixed format is useful when monitoring an instrumentation interface bus. The management lines are best observed in binary format, while the data is more conveniently interpreted in octal, decimal, or hex.

Many logic analyzer applications involve monitoring microprocessor address, data, and control buses. With a general purpose analyzer, the operator must interface his instrument, observing the microprocessor pro-

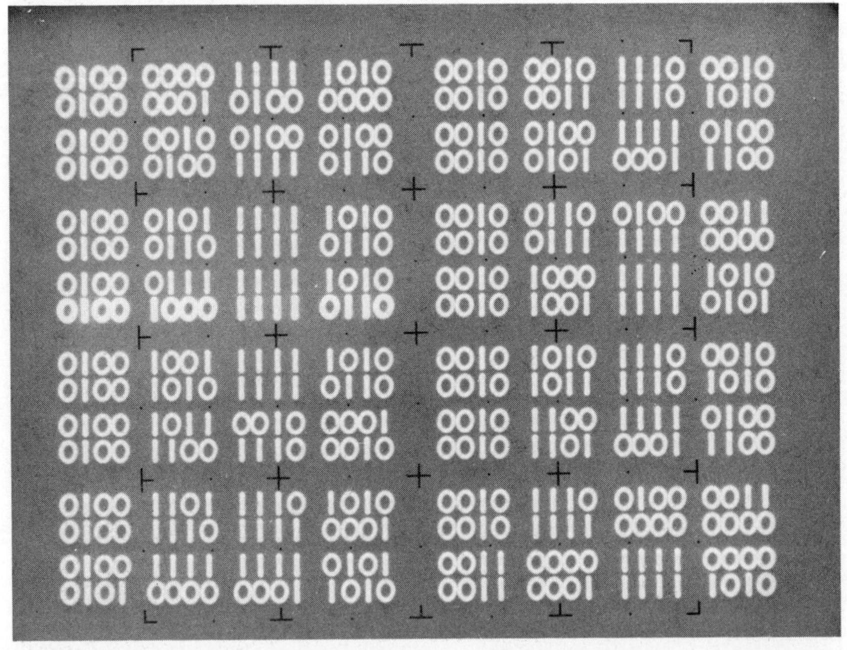

(a)

Fig. 2-2. The list of states can be displayed in a variety of formats. The 1600S logic state analyzer (a) is in binary base. A list display on the 1610A logic state analyzer (b) uses selected bases—hexadecimal (HEX), binary (BIN), octal (OCT), and decimal (DEC). Using a microprocessor-specific personality module of the 1611A logic state analyzer allows complete inverse assembly of data flow for a list display in mnemonics of the target microprocessor (c).

tocol, and translate the trace into the relevant mnemonics, machine cycles, and so forth. Special dedicated logic state analyzers are produced that resolve these problems and present the results as a computer program listing (Fig. 2-2). One major difference between the analyzer listing and the original program is that the program lists all the operations in memory

```
------------TRACE LIST-------------EXCHANGE-COMPLETE----------------
  LABEL       A      C     D    E
   BASE      HEX    BIN   OCT  DEC

 START    ...2850...000...344...1...
  +01        2851   000   010   1
  +02        2852   000   010   1
  +03        2852   000   010   1
  +04     ...2853...000...112...1...
  +05        2853   000   112   1
  +06        2854   000   052   1
  +07        2854   000   052   1
  +08     ...2855...000...372...1...
  +09        2851   000   010   1
  +10        2852   000   010   1
  +11        2852   000   010   1
  +12     ...2853...000...112...1...
  +13        2853   000   112   1
  +14        2854   000   052   1
  +15        2854   000   052   1
  +16     ...2855...000...372...1...
  +17        2851   000   010   1
  +18        2852   000   010   1
  +19        2852   000   010   1
```

(b)

```
                 ADDRESS   DATA   EXTERNAL

     TRIGGER        0B38

-----------------------------------LINE    0---
     ADRS        OPCODE/DATA          EXTERNAL
     0B38        INS  1              0000 0000
     0B39        COM                 0000 0000
     0B3A        SR  4               0000 0000
     0B3B        BZ  0B40            0000 0000
     0B40        LM                  0000 0000
     04D5         00    READ         0000 0000
     0B41        OUTS  0             0000 0000
     0B42        INS  1              0000 0000
     0B43        NI  01              0000 0000
     0B45        LR  J,W             0000 0000
     0B46        LI  A5              0000 0000
     0B48        INC                 0000 0000
     0B49        BNZ  0B48           0000 0000
     0B48        INC                 0000 0000
     0B49        BNZ  0B48           0000 0000
     0B48        INC                 0000 0000
```

(c)

sequence while the analyzer lists the actual sequence of operations. This implies that the logic analyzer will trace microprocessor cycles in addition to tracing the lines in the program listing. For example, a load instruction may use three lines on a program listing:

Address	Op Code/Mnemonic	
A_0	LDA	Load accumulator with contents of
$A_0 + 1$	12	Address high = 12
$A_0 + 2$	34	Address low = 34
$A_0 + 3$	Next	Next instruction

On the analyzer listing, these three lines may become four, the extra cycle displayed being the actual cycle in which the instruction is executed:

Address	Op Code/Mnemonic	
$A_0 +$	LDA }	Could be combined as one line; i.e.,
$A_0 + 1$	12 }	LDA 1234.
$A_0 + 2$	34 }	
1234	Data	Cycle that actually performs instruction
$A_0 + 3$	Next	

Most analyzers have trace and compare modes that permit a trace to be compared with an earlier trace or present stored data. The display may be a conventional list or an exclusive-OR tabular listing of the differences between the two traces with matches displayed as 0's and differences displayed as 1's. The comparison mode is useful for production line testing and fault analysis. New data would be placed in table A and compared to data already stored in table B. The exclusive-OR display would highlight only discrepancies. For finding intermittent faults, a halt A $\neq$ B trigger mode is included. This mode permits the system to run unattended continuously until the fault causes a difference in data contained in table A and table B; the information at this point is frozen for later observation.

Pictorial Displays

Information supplied by the list mode may be too detailed for rapid interpretation. What is needed is some form of pictorial presentation. A graph can be generated with the circuits of Fig. 2-3. The graph highlights the order and flow of the program activity by driving the Y plates of a CRT with the analog equivalent of each memory word. The X plates are driven by a signal corresponding to the memory word selected, i.e., the state-sequence. If the system under test was a simple BCD counter, the graph would commence at the state of all zeros on the lower left hand corner. As the count increased by one with each clock pulse, the dot on the display would move to the right one step and up one step. This would continue until the count of 9, when the counter resets.

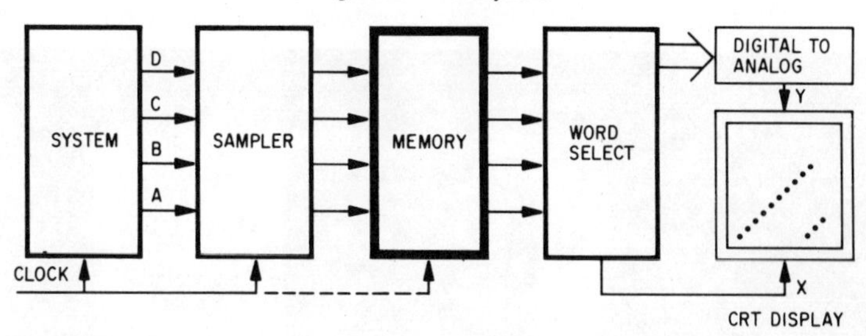

Fig. 2-3. The graph provides a picture of the portion of the data flow sequence. The binary weight of each word in memory is generated via a DAC and fed to the CRT Y plates. The X plates correspond to the word sequence.

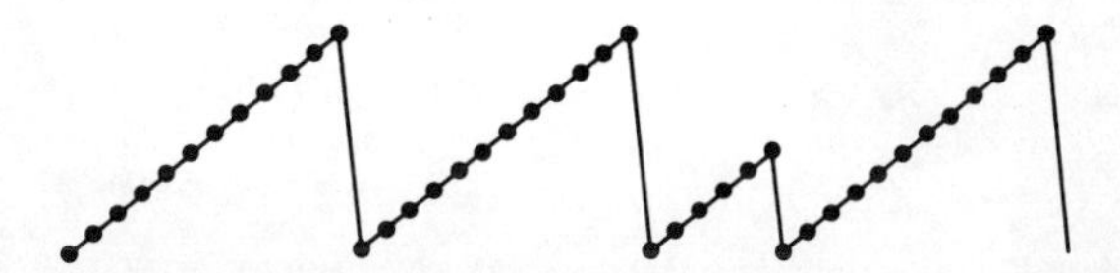

Fig. 2-4. In using the graph mode, the operator looks for unexpected discontinuous lines that may represent jumps or departures from sequential states.

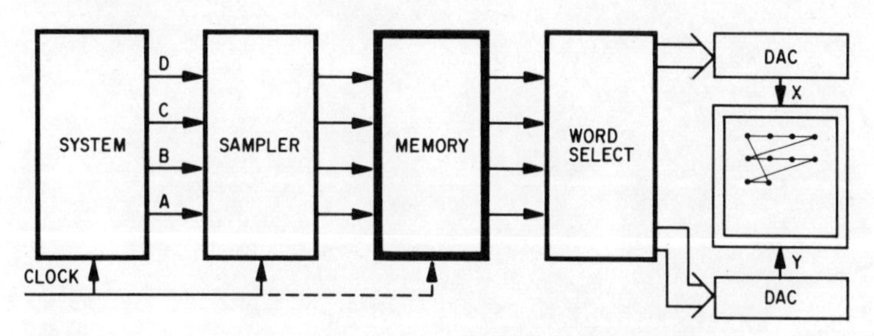

Fig. 2-5. Each half of a word in memory is passed to the X and Y plates of a CRT display via DACs. The resultant position on screen corresponds to the data word. A sequence of words generates a map.

The graph presents a picture of the list, highlighting the data flow sequence. In using the graph mode, the operator looks for unexpected discontinuous lines, as these may represent jumps or departures from sequential states (Fig. 2-4). These discontinuities may not be obvious from the list or table. To provide adequate resolution, the graph has user-defined limits on the vertical axis. Note that increasing the resolution limits the range of active states that may be displayed at one time, and hence, the amount of overview the graph provides. A display that provides the operator with an overview of all active logic states while still providing excellent resolution is the map shown in Fig. 2-5.

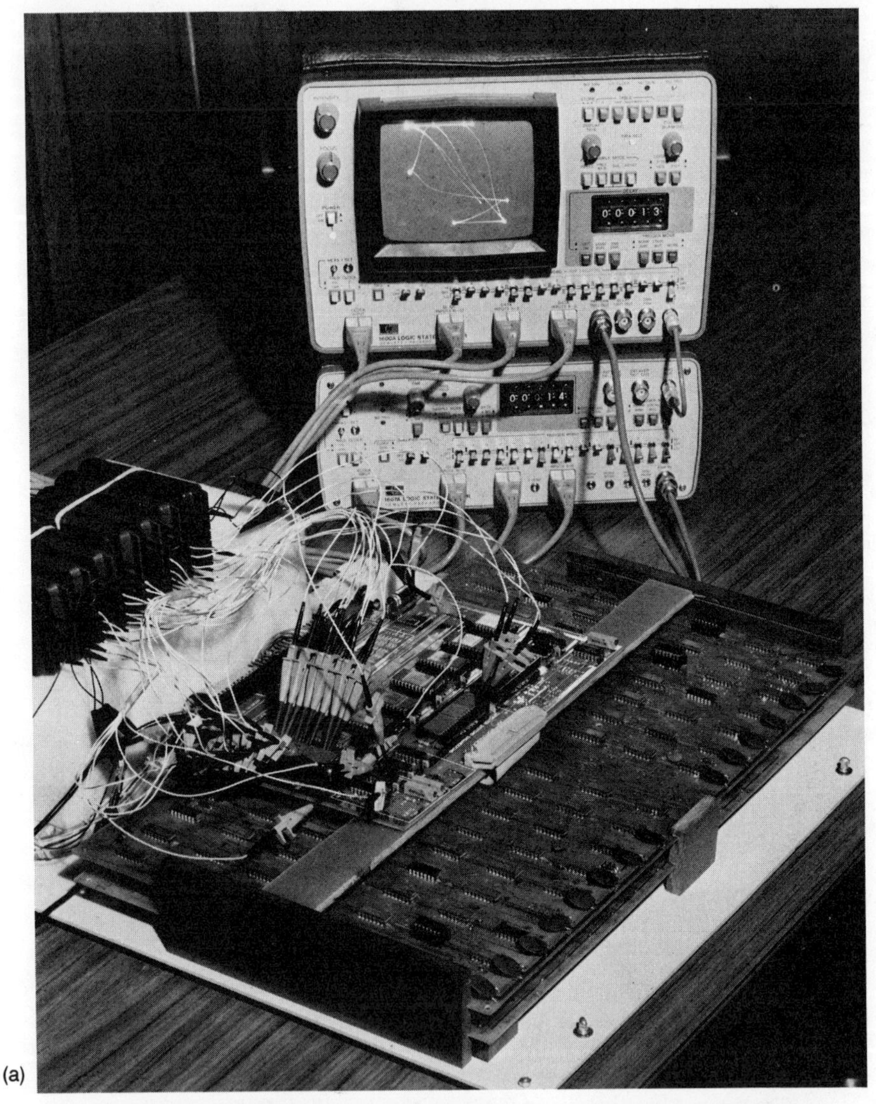

(a)

Fig. 2-6. Each digital system generates its own map, which may be used as a guide in faultfinding. An actual map from a 1600A logic analyzer verifies that the activity is as expected. The word sequence is indicated by connecting each dot with a vector whose brighter end represents the next destination. For the system map shown, an interrupt occurs when the system is in the region of state $2XAX_{16}$. The interrupt vectors are collected from high memory, and the interrupt service routine commences at about location $2X4X_{16}$. Should this fail, the map features will change, and the failures will be readily recognized by the operator.

A map takes the widest possible overview of the activity on the analyzer's data probes. Each memory word is broken down into two, each half driving a digital-to-analog converter (DAC), which in turn drives either the X or Y plates of the CRT. The map shows the presence or absence of entire words, not just individual bits. Unlike the other displays, the most common presentation of the map is in the continuous mode. The dot pattern indicates whether or not the correct activity is taking place, and the dot brightness provides a qualitative indication of the relative word frequency. The word sequence is indicated by connecting each dot with a vector that has a shooting star appearance. The vectors connecting the dots are thicker and brighter toward the next dot in sequence.

On the map display, the data state or memory word of all 0's in positive logic would generate a display dot on the upper left hand corner, while all 1's would generate a dot on the lower right. In Fig. 2-5, the map has been scaled for a four line or 16-bit display. With a BCD counter, the display would start off at the all zero location (00,00), then move to location (01,00), and so forth. For a BCD counter, the circuit is reset following the state (01,10). The display, as shown, represents the map for a BCD counter. Should the counter malfunction, the map will change; this change may be readily detected by even an inexperienced operator. In practice, the map may display more than 16 different states, providing an excellent dynamic overview of the system activity. Other circuits or systems will have their own unique maps. An operator will soon come to recognize the distinctive characteristics of each (Fig. 2-6). The experienced operator will then be able to tell from the map whether the system activity is in the correct states and, from the relative intensity of all dots, the relative time spent in each state.

The three displays discussed illustrate the various forms in which a data domain instrument may present its results. With the simple counting circuit shown, all displays provide essentially the same information. However, in more complex systems the various presentations would complement one another. The map provides a very rapid overview of the activity of the system under test. The graph highlights the data flow sequence, while the list allows a more detailed study of selected activity. If an instrument with

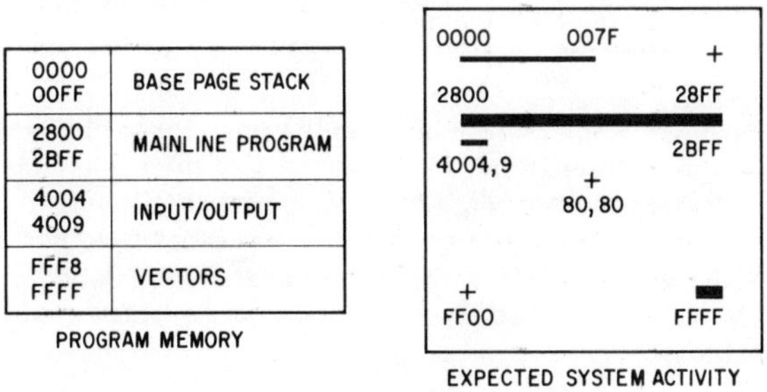

Address	Contents
0000 00FF	BASE PAGE STACK
2800 2BFF	MAINLINE PROGRAM
4004 4009	INPUT/OUTPUT
FFF8 FFFF	VECTORS

PROGRAM MEMORY

0000 007F
2800 28FF
2BFF
4004,9
80, 80
FF00 FFFF

EXPECTED SYSTEM ACTIVITY

(b)

all three features were available in a faultfinding process, the map would be viewed first to gain an overview of the system operation and to pinpoint likely problem areas. The data flow in these problem areas would be examined more closely using the graph. Finally, for the closest examination, the list would be investigated.

2.3 CLOCK CONTROLS

A logic state analyzer must interpret the state of the data in exactly the same manner as the data is interpreted by the system under observation. The interpretation of voltage levels was mentioned in Section 2.1. The time interpretation is achieved by selection of the appropriate clock edge (Fig. 2-7). Since most digital systems are synchronous and use the data states present on a clock edge, it is essential that the state analyzer sample data on this same active edge (Fig. 2-8). In this way, the analyzer traces the data used by the system in its subsequent operations. The appropriate clock transition is selected with a front panel control on the analyzer.

In many digital systems the data bus will be multiplexed; on one clock pulse, the bus contains data from one component, while on a second clock pulse, the data is from a second component. In other systems there may not be valid or new data on the bus for every clock pulse. In either case, unless the clock latching the data into memory is qualified or selectively enabled, the analyzer memory will be loaded with unwanted samples. The data on

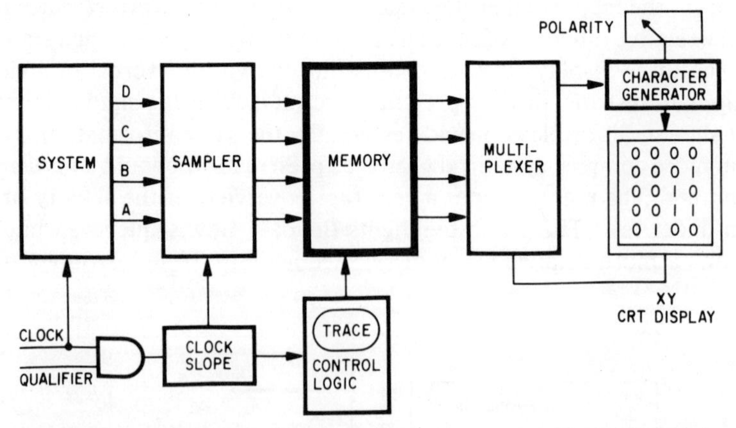

Fig. 2-7. The clock slope control enables the operator to choose to sample data on the positive or negative transition of the system clock. The analyzer is designed with a zero hold time to assure that data is sampled right on the active edge of the system clock. Clock qualifier controls may be set to logic one, logic zero, or "don't care" (off). Data is placed in analyzer memory only when the conditions set by clock qualifier controls are satisfied.

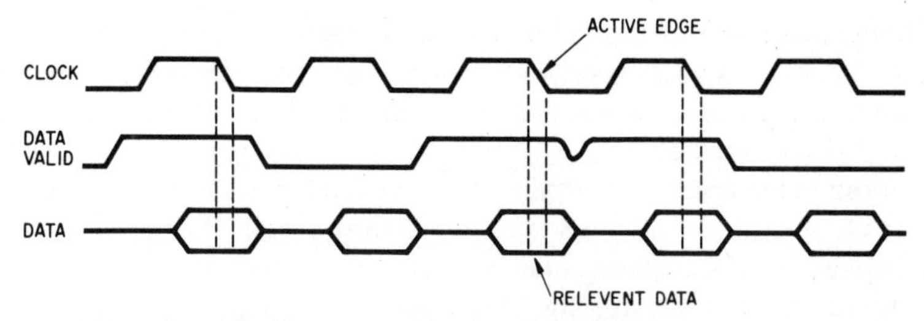

Fig. 2-8. To sample data, a logic state analyzer requires a clock transition when the data is valid. When the data is not valid, or not required on each clock edge, it may be qualified by the clock qualifier.

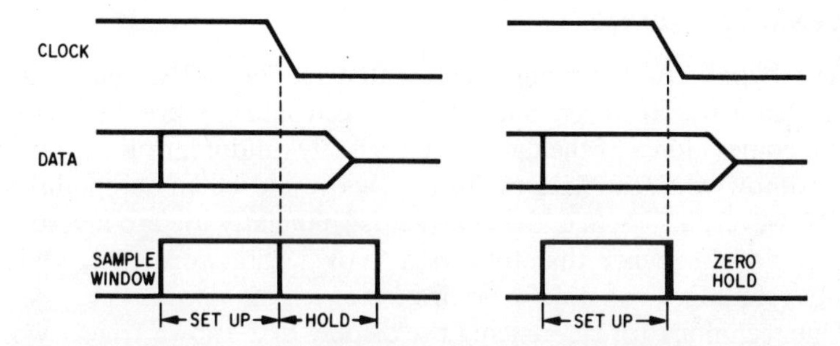

Fig. 2-9. To capture data, a conventional sampling circuit will require the input to be stable for a time prior to the active clock edge and held for a time following that edge. In many digital systems the data changes within a few nanoseconds of the active clock. To assure that the logic state analyzer only traces present data, it must have a zero hold time.

the bus is defined by the status of one or more control lines. These control lines must be logically ANDed with the system clock in order to latch into memory only the required data. This qualifier circuit could be constructed external to the system and the analyzer. This may be the only solution in some complex systems. Normally, one or more clock qualifiers are part of the logic analyzer. The qualifier logic usually has an on-off control for each channel, the on-control having provision for either a logic one or zero. The clock qualifier circuit is sometimes known as a display qualifier, as a sample is taken on the active edge of the clock and hence displayed only if the qualifier conditions are satisfied.

Practical sampling circuits acquire data over some finite time window. One possibility is shown in the first diagram of Fig. 2-9. Sampling commences some time before the active clock and finishes some time afterward. These times are referred to as the set-up and hold times respectively, and the data must be stable during these times. In many systems the data changes state immediately following the active clock edge. In these circumstances, logic state analyzers with positive hold times may trace indeterminate data. To guarantee that only current data is captured, a logic state analyzer must have a zero hold time.

In the schematic of the analyzer, provision has been made to halt the memory clock once the memory is full. To start a trace, the operator would press the trace button, which collects sufficient samples to fill the memory. To retain the continuous display mode, which is particularly useful for the map display, the control logic should also have provision for continuous trace and stop commands.

2.4 TRIGGERING

Basic Triggering

The hypothesized product represented in Fig. 2-7 would be a very useful instrument. However, once enabled, it would capture the first set of data that comes along. If the data were perfectly random, or if the operator does not know what the data might be, this would be an acceptable technique. However, in practice, the analyzer is frequently used to investigate a particular data sequence that follows a known data word; i.e., the trace should be referenced to a unique bit pattern or trigger word.

One technique for referencing the display to a known trigger word is to present that word in a trigger logic circuit and compare this pattern to the final word in the analyzer memory. When the pattern matches the sample, the trigger logic would provide a control signal to halt the trace and hold in

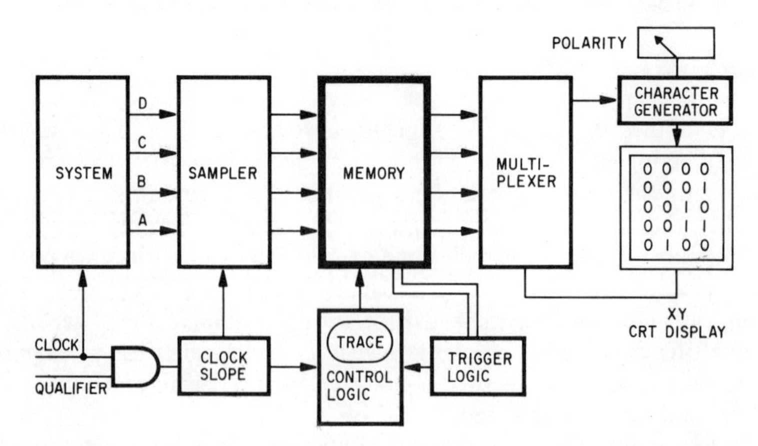

Fig. 2-10. By comparing the word in the final memory position with a preset word, the trace may be made to halt on a preset trigger word. The memory now contains the trigger word and the data following the trigger. However, no real-time signal is available to synchronize time domain instruments.

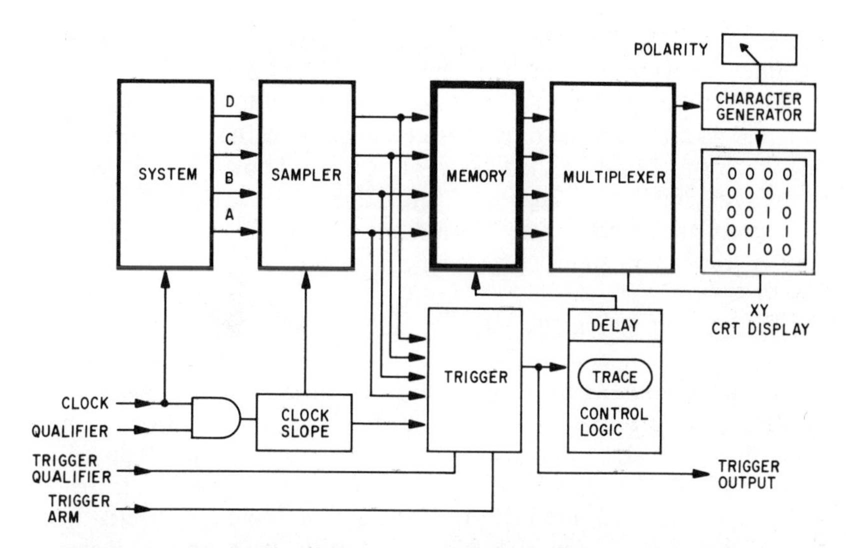

Fig. 2-11. By taking the input to the trigger logic immediately following the sampling circuit, an output signal for synchronizing oscilloscopes may be generated. To freeze the memory in a Trigger Starts Trace mode, a delay circuit counts the progress of the trigger word through the memory, disabling the inputs when the memory has been filled. To provide a Trigger Ends Trace mode, the delay could be set to a count of zero. Data would now ripple through memory until the trigger pattern is recognized, at which time the trace halts. The sequence leading to the trigger word would be frozen in memory. Adding additional delay permits the capture of data well removed from the trigger word. Refinements to the trigger circuits include trigger qualifier and trigger arm (shown) or sequence triggering discussed in the text.

memory the trigger word and the data sequence following that trigger word (Fig. 2-10). This sequence is displayed on the CRT screen. The mode is referred to as the trigger starts trace mode.

The trigger logic proposed in Fig. 2-10 will not provide a real-time synchronizing signal. Such a signal may be required to trigger an external device, such as an oscilloscope, for the display of one data channel in the time domain or to arm a second analyzer for sequential type triggering.

To generate a real-time synchronizing signal, the trigger conditions must be detected as they occur. Shifting the trigger logic to the memory input allows this to happen (Fig. 2-11). Immediately, the trigger logic emits a pulse that provides the synchronizing signal for external devices. This same pulse enables an internal counter delay circuit that keeps track of the number of samples to memory, disabling the inputs when the memory has been filled.

By placing the trigger logic in parallel with the memory, it continues to function and provide external trigger pulses even after the memory is full and the trace complete. On the display, the trigger word will normally be highlighted by being intensified or placed in inverse video.

For each trigger bit there are three control positions to permit triggering on a logic one, logic zero, or don't care. Don't care triggering is appropriate when some part of the trigger word is not known or not pertinent. The analyzer could then trigger on several states. For example, if part of the trigger word was 0XX0, where X is a don't care, an analyzer would trigger on any of the binary states of decimal equivalence 0, 2, 4, or 6, whichever occurs first.

Don't care triggering is useful in faultfinding. By observing the map, the area where problems appear to arise may be deduced. Then a more detailed examination of that region may be undertaken by triggering with some of the values that define that area of the map. If this technique initially does not trigger the analyzer, the triggering may be "relaxed" by placing another bit into the don't care condition. Alternatively, if the data that is traced is of no interest, the investigation could be directed into a region of greater interest by specifying more of the trigger bits as logic ones or zeros.

Use of don't care triggering may require some compromises. For example, consider the case when the trigger could be the hexadecimal word 1234 or 1235. In binary notation the trigger would not be any problem. It is

0001 0010 0011 010X

where X is a don't care. But in hexadecimal format, the trigger 123X would cause all words between 1230_{16} and $123F_{16}$ to act as triggers, not just 1234_{16} and 1235_{16}. A logic analyzer that permits range triggering (greater than and less than triggering) overcomes this frustration, but to add this facility requires further complications and compromises in analyzer design. Alternatively, some instruments allow the operator to define and display parameters in different number bases. In this illustration, the trigger could be defined in binary and the results displayed in hex. Triggering would occur on states 1234_{16} or 1235_{16}, but the hex display would be 123*, with the * indicating that trigger conditions are defined but cannot be written in hex.

The instrument in Fig. 2-11 traces data following the trigger word. In faultfinding it may be known that the system under observation goes to a certain data state where it should not have gone. The question then is, "How did it get there?" By allowing data to ripple through memory and then halting when the trigger conditions are satisfied, the instrument provides a trigger ends trace mode. The memory now contains the trigger word plus the data leading up to that trigger word; i.e., the analyzer has captured negative time data. System crashes may often be trapped with the trigger ends trace mode. Consider the case when the system loses its clock. In the trigger ends trace mode, the analyzer trace will be the sequence preceding the clock failure; once the clock failed, no more data is traced. Alternatively, locations outside the normal program memory may be set up as the trigger. Should the system ever enter this region of memory, the analyzer halts and the sequence that caused the system to go to an unexpected location is trapped in memory for later investigation.

Delayed or Indexed Triggering

To trace a relatively large program, some refinements are necessary if this trace is to be made within the practical limits of analyzer memory depth. One technique is to trap data in some less detail by using clock qualifiers. Selective trace (Section 2.5) can be used to select only specific data. Another technique is to make multiple passes using the final data word of each pass as the trigger word for the next pass. Eventually, by this technique, the complete sequence may be constructed.

There are limitations to investigating program activity by using multiple traces. Should the program contain a loop, none of the addresses within that loop will be unique and, therefore, cannot provide a unique trigger for the next pass. One method to skip or pass loops to reach program activity well removed from a unique trigger word is to use delayed or indexed triggering. A second technique is sequential triggering.

As shown in Fig. 2-12, in the normal Trigger Starts Trace mode, the data words immediately following the trigger are captured. With delay, the analyzer window may be indexed such that data well removed from the trigger word are traced. This is illustrated in the second drawing. In Fig. 2-13 the sequence TRACE is to be captured only after the system passes through the left hand path. This is achieved by triggering on the word 2800_{16} and delaying by the number of clock cycles required to exit the left hand loop.

Most analyzers have a relatively large delay capability provided (64K to 100K) and can probe system activity well removed from the trigger word.

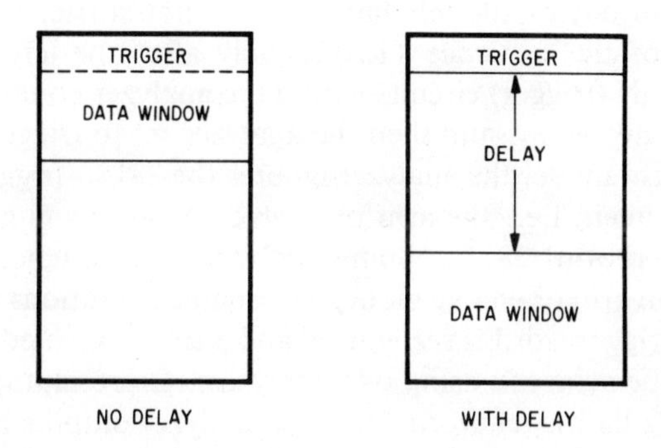

Fig. 2-12. With no delay, the analyzer captures data immediately following the trigger word. With delay, the data window is indexed relative to the trigger as shown.

In practice, there may be limitations to using digital delay. Very few programs contain loops as simple as that of Fig. 2-13, and the number of times through the loop may vary dependent upon some additional conditions. Under these circumstances, the sequence TRACE cannot be defined by the trigger word 2800_{16} and a given fixed digital delay. A sequential trigger is necessary (refer to Section 2.4). If the analyzer is used in the Trigger Ends Trace mode, the trigger word may be placed in the center of the display by using a small delay.

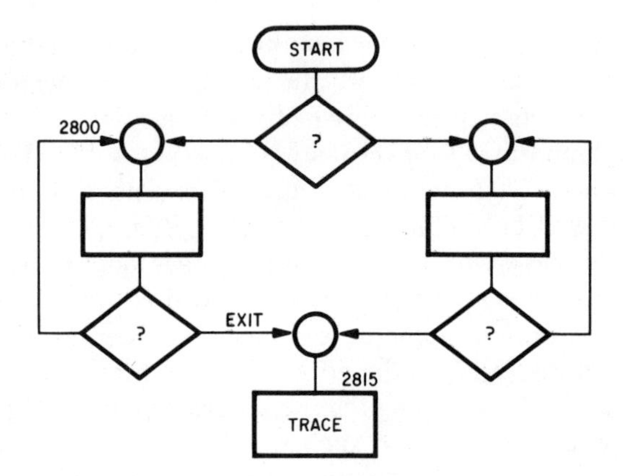

Fig. 2-13. To capture the sequence called TRACE only after the system has passed through the left hand loop, the trigger word could be set to 2800_{16} and the delay set to the total number of clock cycles between the state 2800_{16} and 2815_{16}.

Arming and Sequential Triggering

One necessary requirement for a logic analyzer is the ability to trigger on a sequence of words. For example, in the program of Fig. 2-13, if the number of executions of the left hand loop is not sufficiently defined to permit capture of the sequence TRACE only after the left hand path is taken, special logic (trigger) circuits within the analyzer could be set to arm on the logical state 2800_{16}, and then the analyzer set to trigger on the state 2815_{16}. In this arm mode, the analyzer ignores the 2815_{16} trigger if the right hand path was taken; i.e., the arm or enable conditions must be satisfied before the trigger word 2815_{16}. Some analyzers are designed with trigger logic including an arm or enable mode. The enable conditions must be satisfied before the trigger word is recognized and a trace executed. Alternatively, arming may be achieved using two analyzers. On receipt of the first bit pattern matching its trigger word, the first analyzer outputs a signal on its pattern trigger output (PTO) line. The PTO line is connected to the TRIG ARM input of the second analyzer (Fig. 2-11). Upon receipt of the arming signal, the second analyzer now executes a trace when its trigger conditions are satisfied.

Arming is not reserved to state analyzers. One very important application arises when a state analyzer is used to arm a timing analyzer, or vice versa. This will be discussed in Chap. 3.

With complex software, the two level triggering provided by the arming may not be adequate. For example, to execute a trace only after the system has followed path #2 as defined in Fig. 2-14, all other paths must be excluded. The analyzer needs to trace only after the states 2849_{16}, $284C_{16}$, and $284E_{16}$ are found in sequence.

If the analyzer displays the data associated with the addresses given in the trigger sequence, this mode may be used to acquire data used in later routines. For example, in Fig. 2-15 the parameters are loaded at steps $286A_{16}$, $286D_{16}$, and 2877_{16}, and the routine in question starts at location $29A7_{16}$. Using the triggering specifications shown, the analyzer lists all the parameters plus the trace. In the example illustrated, a state counter has been enabled. This shows 1509 states between the acquisition of the first parameter at address $286A_{16}$ and the start of the multiplication routine. Without the extensive triggering capability to capture these parameters, a memory of more than 1600 states would be required. Parameters further back would increase the memory requirements.

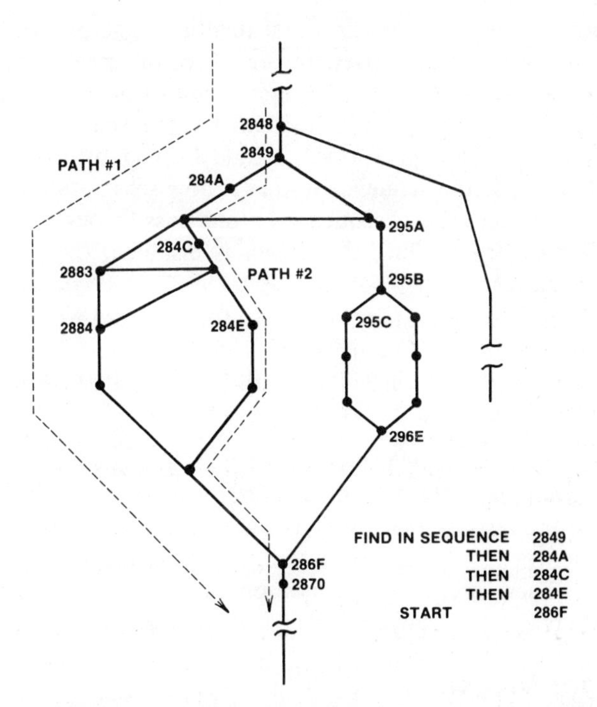

Fig. 2-14. A trace may be taken after a pass through a specified path of a complex branching network with the sequential triggering sequence shown.

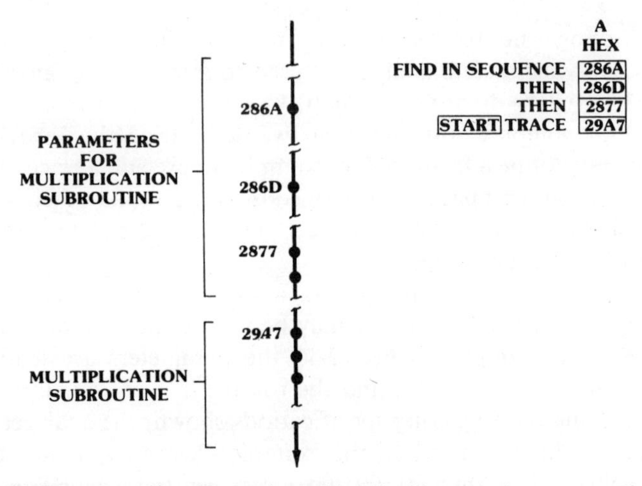

Fig. 2-15. Trace specification and resulting list illustrate how sequential triggering may be used with a 1610A logic analyzer to gather parameters used in a later program subroutine.

In many complex networks, the sequential triggering requirement may be met by using multiple entries. In Fig. 2-16, this problem may be overcome with an analyzer that has a sequence restart or trigger disable. Without sequence restart, a pass on path #1 satisfies the first two sequence terms; the remainder of the trigger words would be met by a subsequent pass through path #3. If the sequence restart is now set to state 2870_{16}, the analyzer must find the trigger sequence on one pass through the network before executing a trace. Once the trigger is disabled, the trigger sequence must start again.

The sequence restart may be used to trace a pass through a zero length path where there are no unique points to define the sequence (Fig. 2-17). With this network, once the 2849_{16} conditions are satisfied on each following word the analyzer will

(a) Check the start sequence. If the word is $287C_{16}$, the analyzer will commence a trace. If it is not, the analyzer will

(b) Check the restart conditions. If these are not met, the analyzer looks for the word 2849_{16} again. In this case the sequence restart is all don't cares. Therefore, unless condition (a) was satisfied (i.e., the zero length path), the analyzer will always restart.

Count Triggering

A network often encountered is the nested loop illustrated in Fig. 2-18. If an analyzer has a pass count in the trigger logic, it is possible to

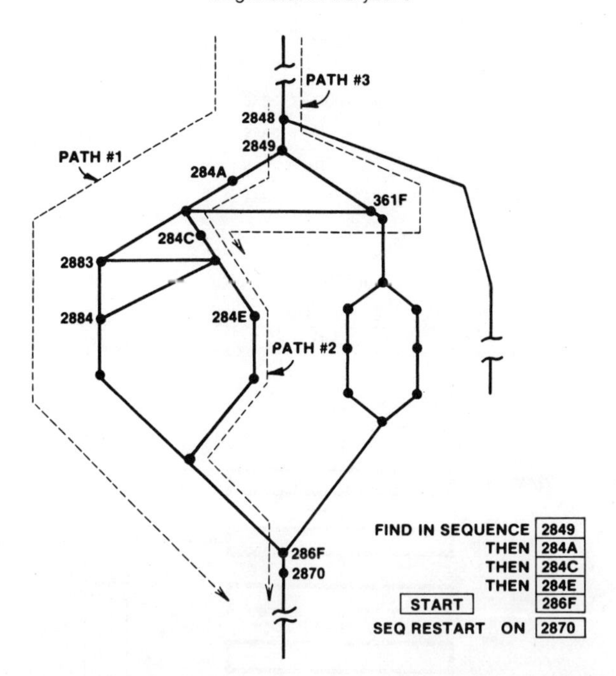

Fig. 2-16. Trace specification for tracing a specific path in a branching network and using a sequence restart on an exit state to guarantee that the specific path is satisfied after only one pass through the network.

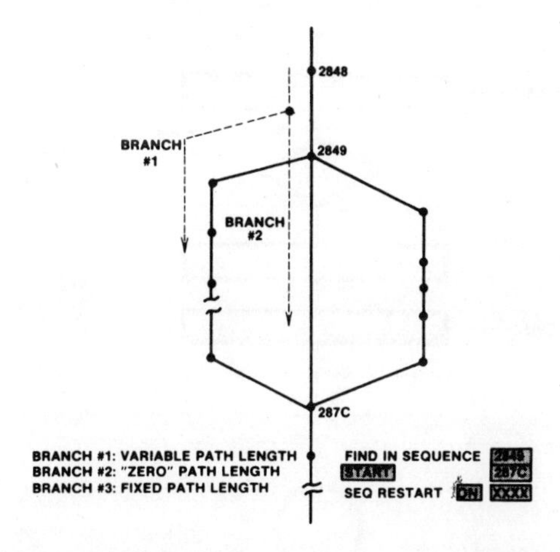

Fig. 2-17. Trace specification for tracing a zero length branch (direct jump) using sequence restart.

2830

(a)

	OCCUR DEC
FIND IN SEQUENCE 2830	1
THEN 28AE	9
THEN 28A5	8
START TRACE 2841	7

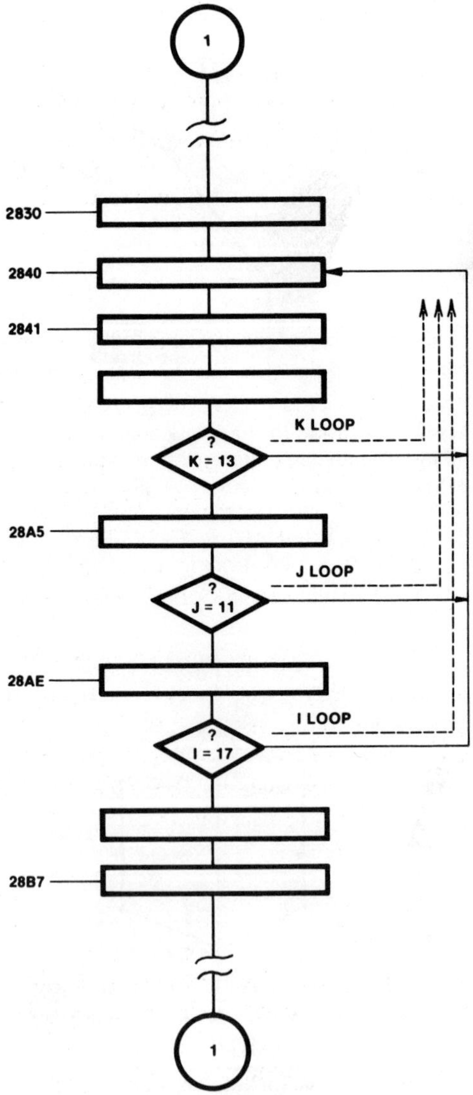

(b)

Fig. 2-18. With the trace specification shown a logic analyzer will acquire data at specified passes through each loop.

examine program activity in, for example, the 9th pass of the I loop, the 8th pass of the J loop, and the 7th pass of the K loop.

The trace specification illustrated in Fig. 2-18 will direct the analyzer to acquire data at state 2841_{16} only when these conditions are met. The state 2830_{16} is specified to ensure that the analyzer does not enter midway in the execution of the nested loop. Without the occurrence count on the trigger, a very large memory is necessary to include data on the specified pass about the word $28AE_{16}$. Infinite operator patience is also necessary to search that memory for the data required.

Digital delay may be implemented with a pass count by specifying a sequence state of all don't cares, and then setting the delay using the occurrence counter. For example, formatting an analyzer to find the first occurrence of the word $284B_{16}$ and starting the trace on the 837th occurrence of the word XXXX_{16} is equivalent to a trigger word of $284B_{16}$ and a delay of 837_{10}.

Trigger Qualifiers

Most analyzers also have trigger qualifiers similar to those for the clock or display. With a trigger qualifier, the analyzer will only trigger or freeze the data in memory when both the trigger *and* qualifier conditions are satisfied together.

Triggering qualifiers extend the trigger word width by an additional channel for every qualifier input, increasing the flexibility in triggering and, hence, in data collection. The qualifier signals are not displayed and require no memory space. Note that qualifying the trigger does not alter the display. However, the trigger will be qualified by the clock or display qualifiers.

The trigger qualifier is useful in observing microprocessor systems. If, for example, two subroutines are stored back to back, in the execution of the return from subroutine (RTS) of subroutine 1 the look-ahead feature of some microprocessors will put the address SUB2 on the bus. A logic state analyzer with SUB2 as the trigger will execute a trace both at the conclusion of subroutine 1 and at the start of subroutine 2.

SUB1	
	RTS
SUB2	
	RTS

However, there are differences. When the address SUB2 occurs on the address bus in the execution of subroutine 2, it is an op code fetch, and many microprocessors have a control to specify an op code fetch. In the 6502, for example, the SYNC line will go high. Using this control line as a trigger qualifier enables the analyzer to execute a trace only on subroutine 2; should the address SUB2 occur as a consequence of the previous RTS instruction, the SYNC line is low. Hence, the trigger qualifier conditions are not satisfied and no trace occurs.

Conclusion

A simple system may be traced by triggering on a single trigger word. The trigger word may start or end the trace. This trigger word will normally be highlighted on the display by intensified or inverse video. If some restrictions are required on the trigger word, the triggering may be further restricted by using trigger qualifiers. To reach program activity well removed from a unique trigger word, delay or indexed triggering is used. For tracing more complex program activity, analyzers with arming, sequential triggering and sequence restart, and multiple occurrence triggering are required. The triggering capability is one of the most important attributes of a logic analyzer. Without adequate triggering it is very difficult to observe the desired regions of system activity.

2.5 SELECTIVE TRACING

When monitoring a digital system, a logic analyzer will trap a large quantity of data. The operator must then edit this data; a better alternative is to perform some of this editing within the instrument. This is known as selective trace; logic circuits within the analyzer select only the desired data and store this in the memory. The memory stores quality data rather than a large quantity of unrequired data.

One common measurement in the selective trace mode is to trace only trigger words. In general, using a fully defined trigger word results in insufficient range of samples for a program overview. A sufficient number of states can be obtained to define program direction by inserting some don't cares in the trigger word. For example, if a trigger word is defined as $12X4_{16}$, only the states 1204_{16}, 1214_{16}, 1224_{16} . . . $12F4_{16}$ will be traced. These states will be more than adequate to functionally describe the activity through this region of the program. If the program were sequential and all states were traced, the display would be 1200_{16}, 1201_{16}, 1202_{16}, . . . through to $12FF_{16}$; 256 words would have to be searched and deciphered to obtain the same functional result as that obtained with the 16 word trace triggers.

Combining the trace triggers mode with digital delay provides a trace events mode. The events traced will now be every nth bit following the trigger word, where n is set by the delay control. Should a system routine under test contain many branches, the appropriate selection of trigger word and delay present an overall picture of program activity.

The more sophisticated logic state analyzers have provision for tracing only specified states. These analyzers may have a multiple occurrence counter on each of the trace-only states. Therefore, the specified states are only acquired after they have occurred the number of times set in the counters. This form of selective trace may be considered a software operation. Data enters the analyzer and is compared with the trace-only conditions. If these conditions are satisfied, the data will be placed in the memory; if they are not satisfied, the data is disregarded.

Clock qualifier(s) also perform a selective trace function even though the clock qualifier is a hardware operation. Data is acquired dependent upon the state of particular line(s) hardwired to the qualifier input(s). The example given in Section 2.3 employed a microprocessor control line as a qualifier. If the qualifiers were connected to some of the microprocessor address lines, only a selected range of addresses would be traced by the analyzer. In this case, there would be no distinction between the clock qualifier and selective trace modes.

2.6 COUNT MEASUREMENTS

Larger analyzers have provision for making count measurements, both state and time, in either the relative or absolute mode. These measure-

(a)

		STATE COUNT REL
SEQUENCE	28B7	
SEQUENCE	28AE	1287
SEQUENCE	28A5	104
START	2841	7
+01	0000	0
+02	2842	0

			STATE COUNT ABS
SEQUENCE	28B7	-	1398
SEQUENCE	28AE	-	111
SEQUENCE	28A5	-	7
START	2841	+	0
+01	0000	+	0
+02	2842	+	0

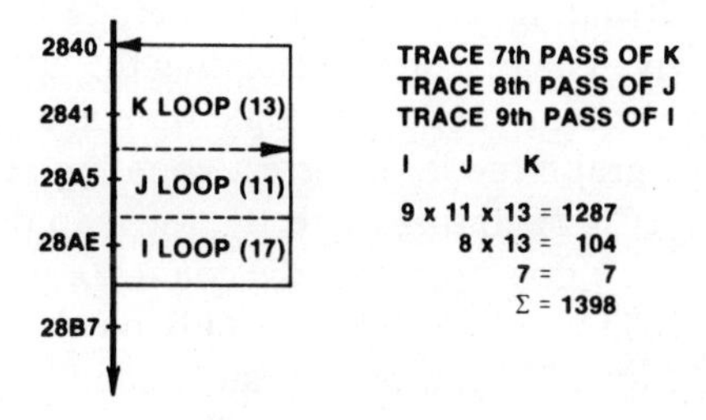

(b)

Fig. 2-19. Calculation of how many times state 2840_{16} of the innermost loop occurs before the specified trace begins, and part of the resultant trace list in both the relative count and absolute count mode of state 2840_{16}.

ments may be used to provide insight into which computer or microprocessor gives the best performance and to help optimize programs by detecting slow, inefficient subroutines.

To count the number of times a subroutine is called in a program, the analyzer is placed into the Count Triggers mode, using a unique state in the subroutine as a trigger. The program limits are set by the trigger enable and disable. The count is the number of occurrences of the trigger word between the trigger enable and disable.

To verify that the nested loop program of Fig. 2-18 actually executed the number of loops specified, the analyzer could count the number of occurrences of state 2840_{16} and compare this to the expected number. Figure 2-19 shows how the results may be presented. There are 1287 counts of the state 2840_{16} between 2887_{16} and the 9th occurrence of $28A3_{16}$. From the absolute results there are 1398 occurrences of 2840_{16} between states 2887_{16} and 2841_{16} where the trace commenced.

2.7 INTERACTIVE OSCILLOSCOPE/ANALYZER MEASUREMENTS

In most digital systems, an analysis of the state flow highlights any problem areas. If these state problems are suspected to arise from time dependent phenomenon—such as voltage level, pulse width, rise time, overshoot, or noise on one or more of the signal lines—these lines may be investigated in greater detail using either an oscilloscope or a timing analyzer. The oscilloscope is the most useful instrument if the operation can be repeated and each signal line observed independently. However, the timing analyzer is necessary if the timing between signals is important, if negative time is required, or if rapid phenomenon (such as glitches) must be detected (see Section 3.7). To synchronize either instrument with the state flow problem areas, the real-time trigger output from the state analyzer is used.

As an example of how a logic analyzer may be used to trigger an oscilloscope to aid faultfinding, consider a two-decade BCD counter that is not operating correctly. The first step in isolating the problem is to obtain a system overview. In the map mode, the logic state analyzer highlights any missing states; in the graph mode, incorrect counting sequences would be obvious. If the counter is operating correctly, the map of Fig. 2-20a would be obtained. The top left dot represents the count 00, while the lower right dot represents the BCD count of 99. The tails on the dots show the sequence. The map of Fig. 2-20b indicates a faulty counter. The counter skips from state 59 (0101 1001) to state 70 (0111 0000) without passing through states 60 to 69.

Having determined that the fault is somehow related to state 59, this state is made the trigger word. Every time the BCD counter goes to the state 59, the logic analyzer emits a trigger output pulse to trigger an oscilloscope. The oscilloscope probe(s) can now be stepped through all the counter lines

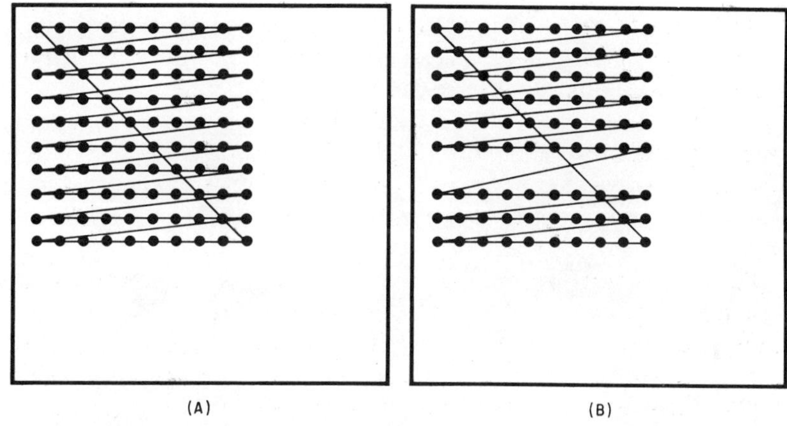

Fig. 2-20. (a) The expected map for a two-decade BCD counter has a dot in every location corresponding to the decimal numbers 0 through 99. (b) In a faulty counter some of these states may be missing.

in turn. On one of the counter data or control lines, the microscopic examination with the oscilloscope should reveal some abnormality that is causing the counter to malfunction.

The logic analyzer pinpointed the location of the problem. Then the pattern recognition and triggering capability of the analyzer referenced the oscilloscope to the appropriate digital time frame. Without the logic analyzer, the only solution may have been to single shot the counter clock.

Note that the analyzer continues to output a trigger pulse when the trigger conditions are met even after a trace has been frozen, permitting observation of repetitive signals on a standard oscilloscope.

2.8 MONITORING COMPUTER SYSTEMS

Introduction

The majority of modern digital systems contains some form of computer, such as a microprocessor. The complete development of such a system requires extensive simulation, emulation, and analysis. A few development systems have been designed to tackle all three jobs; most, however, do not. The analysis capability is more than adequately performed by a logic state analyzer, providing not only a global overview of the complete system operation but also a detailed examination of the program flow and efficiency. Once the design is frozen and goes into production (and later to customers), the state analyzer will be necessary for production testing and field service. Since at some time in its life a microprocessor product may require monitoring by a logic state analyzer, it is wise to consider this interface in the original design.

Dedicated analyzers are available that simply plug into the microprocessor socket on the system to be tested (Fig. 2-21). The analyzer may

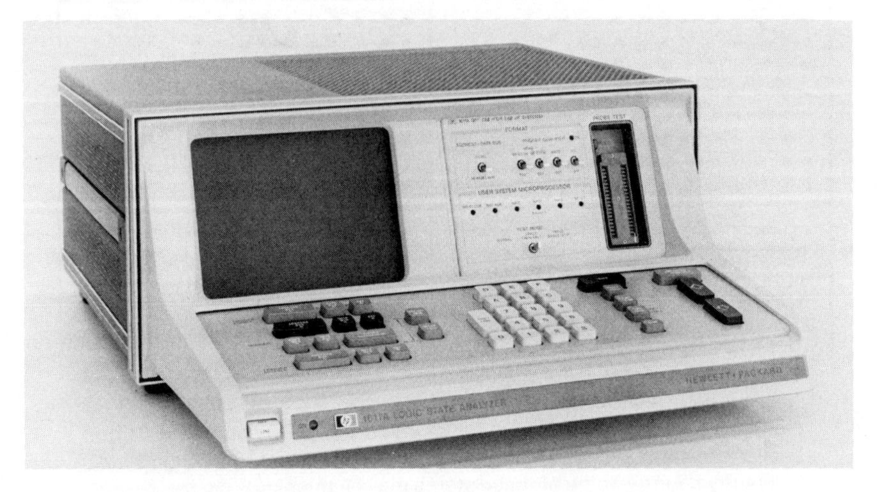

Fig. 2-21. Hewlett-Packard Model 1611A Option Z80 logic state analyzer is an example of a dedicated analyzer. It is used with Z80 microprocessor systems only.

then be used to trace selected portions of program flow, to count specified states, and to time between events. These dedicated instruments may only be used with systems containing microprocessor types for which the operator has the appropriate personality modules. When only a general purpose analyzer is available, the analyzer probes must be connected to the appropriate microprocessor lines and the display visually decoded into microprocessor mnemonics by the operator.

The following examples illustrate the interface between a logic state analyzer with two different microprocessors and a minicomputer. The preprocessing in these examples is not extensive. Refer to Chap. 4 for examples of preprocessing the handshake lines on an instrumentation bus before it is traced by the analyzer.

Example 1: MOS Technology MCS 6502

One of the easiest microprocessors to monitor with a logic analyzer is the MCS 6502. The waveforms of the MCS 6502 are shown in Fig. 2-22. When observing the waveforms for any system, the first question that must be answered is, "What clock or control line has an active edge when all the address and data lines are valid?" With the 6502, the address lines are set up by the $\emptyset_1$ clock while the data is enabled onto the data bus by the $\emptyset_2$ clock. Both the address and data are valid on the negative transition of the $\emptyset_2$ clock. Even if a second transition were available, the negative transition of the $\emptyset_2$ clock should be chosen as the analyzer clock since the microprocessor interprets data on this edge. It is important that any measurement instru-

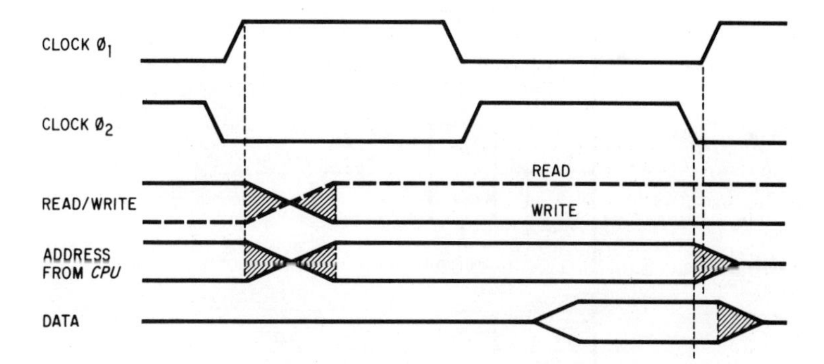

Fig. 2-22. Timing for the 6502 microprocessor. The address and data bus may be sampled on the negative edge of the $\emptyset_2$ clock. The R/W control signal can be used to qualify the trace for read only or write only operations.

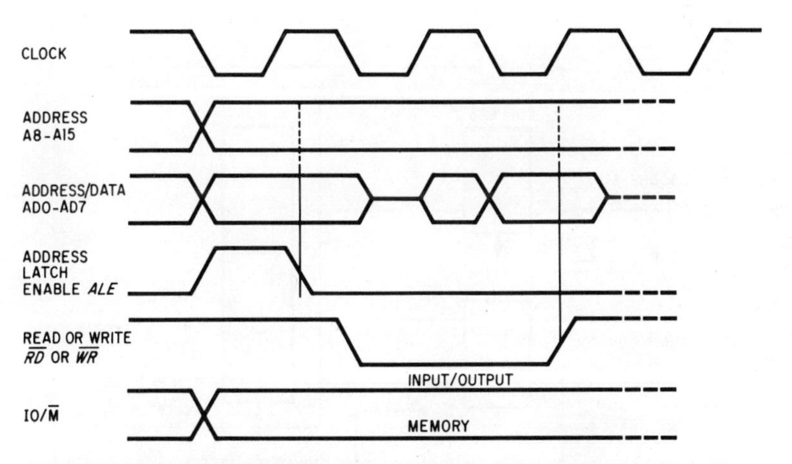

Fig. 2-23. Timing for the 8085 microprocessor. The lower byte of the address and the data are time-division multiplexed on the one bus. The address must be sampled on the negative transition of the address latch enable (ALE), while the data is sampled on either the rising edge of the "not read" or "not write" lines as appropriate.

ment puts exactly the same interpretation on the data as the device under test. Notice that the address and data lines are not guaranteed to be valid for more than a few nanoseconds following the $\emptyset_2$ clock. Therefore, any analyzer used must be capable of monitoring zero hold time signals.

The R/W line can be used to qualify the analyzer clock or trigger for read only (R/W high) or write only (R/W low) operations. Other combinations are possible, although they are not shown on the timing diagram. For example, the 6502 has a SYNC signal that could be used to qualify the clock or trigger on only op code fetches.

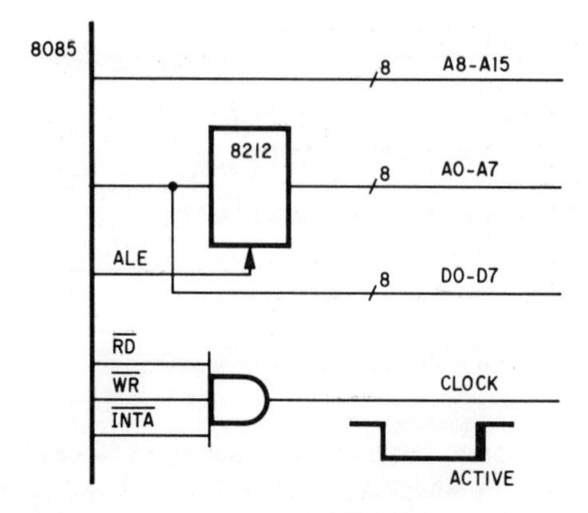

Fig. 2-24. Circuit to interface a logic state analyzer to a 8085 microprocessor.

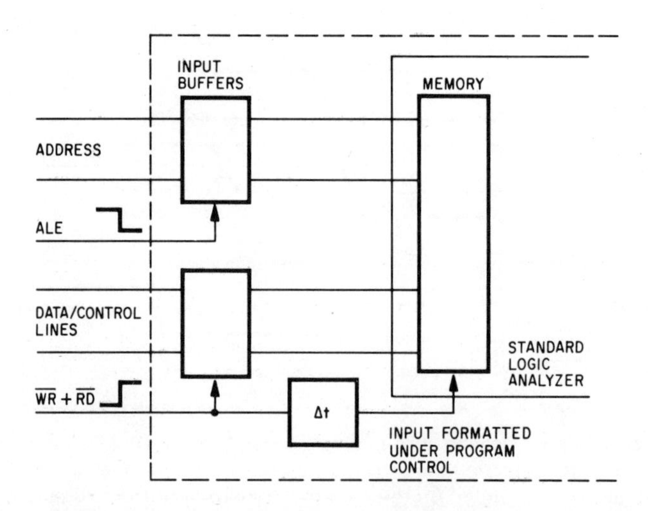

Fig. 2-25. Multiple clock analyzer may be formatted with software to monitor 8085 microprocessor. Address information is sampled on negative transition of ALE while data is sampled on positive transition of either the $\overline{WR}$ or $\overline{RD}$ control lines. The address and data are then transferred to memory by a delayed version of the combination $\overline{WR}$ + $\overline{RD}$ clock.

Example 2: Intel 8085

A second microprocessor, one that requires additional circuit components, is the Intel 8085. This microprocessor multiplexes the low address and data on the one bus (Fig. 2-23). The address is captured on the negative-going transition of the address latch enable (ALE) line, while the data is captured on the low to high transition of either the $\overline{RD}$ or $\overline{WR}$ lines. If interrupts are to be observed, data will also be valid on the positive edge of the interrupt acknowledge line. The circuit to interface the 8085 to a logic state analyzer is shown in Fig. 2-24. If the system to be tested contains system components other than the 8085 components, an 8-bit latch equivalent to the Intel 8212 may already be provided. In that case, only the three input AND gate must be added to provide an interface to a logic analyzer.

The 8085 trace can be qualified by using the appropriate states of the $\overline{\text{RD}}$, $\overline{\text{WR}}$, or $\overline{\text{INTA}}$ lines as the clock. Alternatively, the two status lines could be used to qualify on reads, writes, or op code fetches. The Intel 8085 separates memory from I/O devices; the two operations could be qualified using the IO/$\overline{\text{M}}$.

The 8085 may also be monitored with a multiple clock analyzer eliminating the need for the preprocessor circuit (Fig. 2-25). With multiple clocks, the address information would be programmed to clock into the analyzer buffers on the negative transition of ALE while the data and status lines would be sampled with the positive transition of either the $\overline{\text{RD}}$ *or* the $\overline{\text{WR}}$ control lines. One clock must be chosen as the master to align the address and data since the data lags its associated address. To align the two on the display the combination $\overline{\text{RD}}$ and $\overline{\text{WR}}$ clock should be chosen as the master to transfer data from the analyzer input buffers to the memory.

Example 3: PDP-11 Minicomputer

Figure 2-26 gives the waveforms for several of the signals on the PDP-11 Unibus. In the PDP-11, any device on the bus may act as master while all other devices act as slaves. Each control signal issued by the master must be acknowledged by the (selected) slave. In a read operation, the master places the address onto the 18 lines of the Unibus. For a read, control line 1 will go high. After allowing these lines time to settle, the master will pull the master sync (MSYN) low (i.e., assert MSYN) to instruct the slave to place data on the 16 data lines. A master read is defined by control line 1. When the slave has placed data onto the bus, the slave sync (SSYN) is pulled low (asserted). To allow the lines time to settle, the master waits 75 ns before reading the data and negating the MSYN to acknowledge. The slave completes the operation by releasing the data lines and negating its SSYN signal.

From Fig. 2-26a it is seen that a logic state analyzer could be clocked on the rising edge of MSYN. However, as shown in Fig. 2-26b for the write operation, once the slave has accepted the new data, the master removes the data and negates the MSYN signal. The data and MSYN could be removed in any sequence. Consequently, the rising edge of MSYN cannot be used as the clock for a logic analyzer on a write cycle. One suitable edge would be the falling edge of the MSYN.

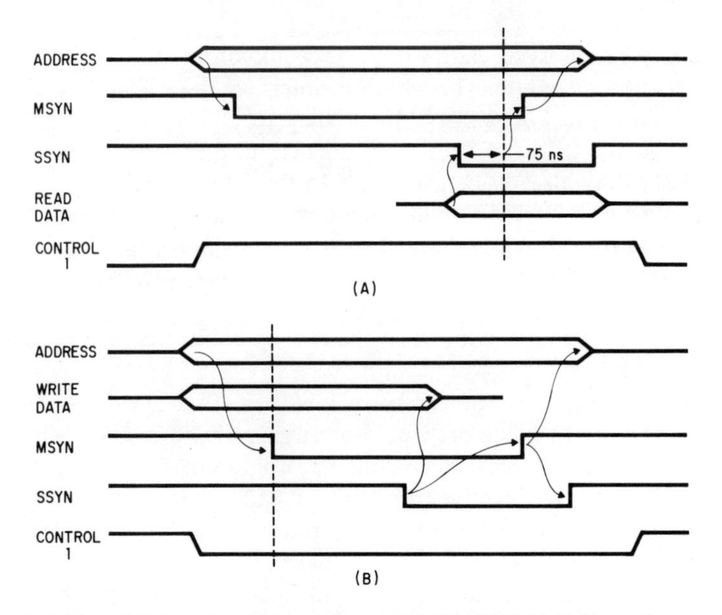

Fig. 2-26. Read and write waveforms for the PDP-11 Unibus. For read operations (a) the address and data are valid on the positive transition of the master sync (MSYN) while on write operations (b) the address and data are valid on the negative transition.

The preprocessing circuit that generates the necessary multiphase ORed qualified clock for the PDP-11 is shown in Fig. 2-27. This circuit is glitch-free, compared to executing the ORing with standard gates. Note that adding the circuits shown to the input of an analyzer will compromise the set-up and hold times. They are best implemented with Schottky devices.

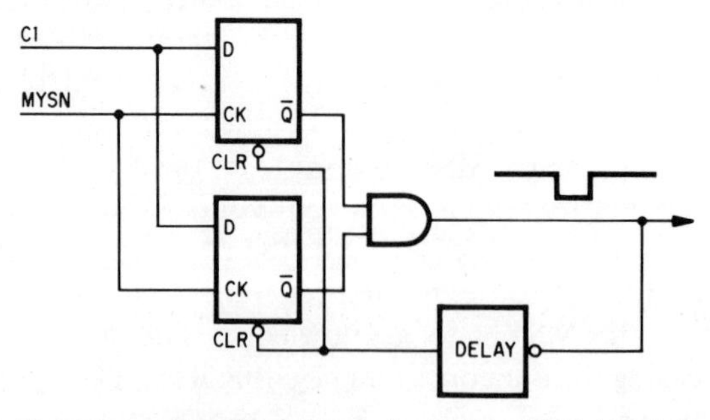

Fig. 2-27. Multiphase ORed qualified clock for a PDP-11 minicomputer. A positive transition on MSYN will clock the output low only if the read-write line (control 1) is high (read). The output will go high after a time determined by the digital delay. A negative transition on MSYN only gives an output pulse when the control line is low (write). The hold time on the address and data buses following the rising edge of MSYN may be zero. If so, additional buffering must be placed on the probes to these lines to compensate for delays in the clock preprocessing circuit shown.

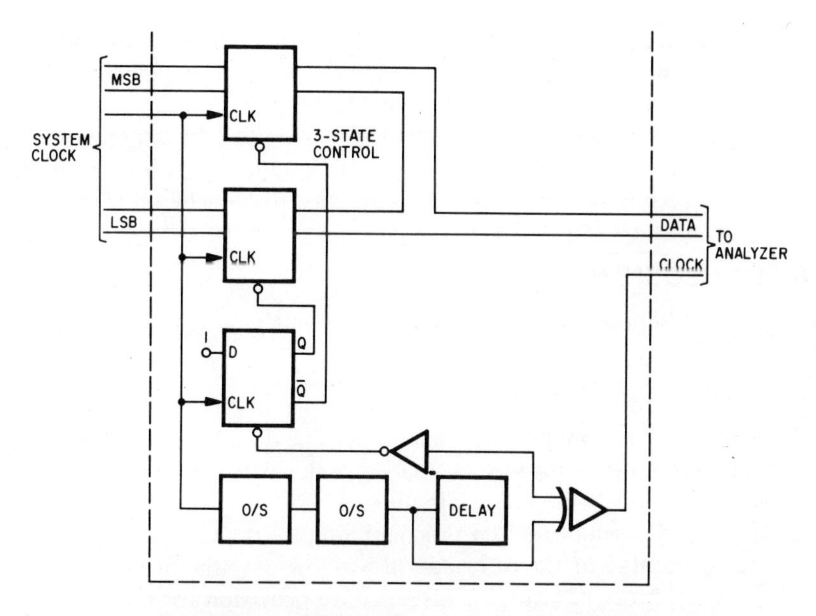

Fig. 2-28. Preprocessor to interweave wide words.

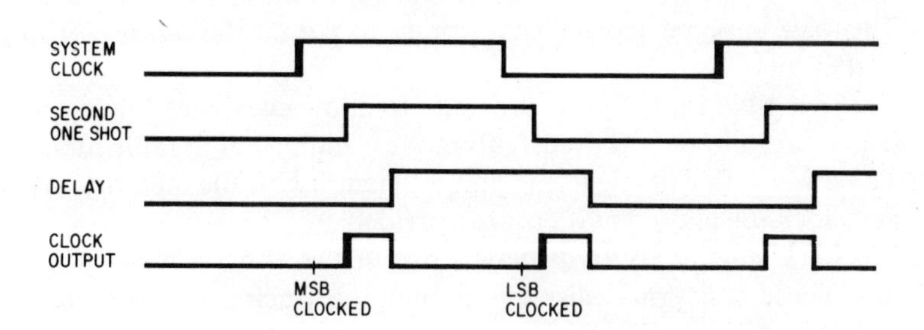

Fig. 2-29. The 1602A analyzer displays two lines of data. With the preprocessor, this facility may be used to display both samples at once rather than having an interweaved display.

Example 4: Interweaving for Wide Words

Digital systems tend to grow in complexity. To analyze more channels than available on an analyzer, the wide words may be interleaved or multiplexed into two. The circuit to do this is shown in Fig. 2-28. On the active system clock, data is strobed into the three state latches. The most significant data is also enabled to the preprocessor output by the D flip-flop (or "one-shot"). After a delay set by the first one-shot, the preprocessor outputs one clock. Data should be sampled into the logic analyzer on the rising edge of this pulse. After a time determined by the delay circuit, the D flip-flop is cleared, enabling the least significant data to the preprocessor output. This data would be clocked to the analyzer on the next generated clock, which occurs when the second one-shot times out (Fig. 2-29).

Since the analyzer trace consists of two samples taken in one time interval, the analyzer's bandwidth is halved. For optimum performance, the width of the second one-shot should be adjusted to 1/f where f is the maximum analyzer frequency.

2.9 CONCLUSION

This chapter contains a discussion of the logic state analyzer. In summary:

(1) The analyzer is multinodal, enabling the observation of data on systems such as microprocessor buses. The data is interpreted by the analyzer input comparators that may have variable thresholds to accommodate different logic families.

(2) Unique triggering or pattern recognition plus digital delay will permit the positioning of the information window over the program area in question. More advanced analyzers have provision for recognition of a sequence of pattern or trigger words before a trace is executed. They may also count on time events between specified word patterns.

(3) The logic analyzer has internal storage to permit the capture of single shot events.

(4) Negative time capability is provided to allow events leading up to the trigger word to be captured. This mode is important in faultfinding.

(5) To permit efficient triggering and efficient use of the memory, trigger and clock (display) qualifiers are provided.

(6) The logic state analyzer displays its results as either a map, graph, or list. These functional displays permit the tracing of program flow while magnifying errors.

(7) To trace data on the same active clock edge as is used by the system under test, the analyzer has a clock edge select control. To avoid tracing indeterminate or wrong data, the analyzer should have a zero hold time.

(8) To permit observation of a single channel in the time domain, the analyzer has a trigger output to synchronize the time domain instruments to a specified state sequence.

CHAPTER THREE

Logic Timing Analyzers

3.1 INTRODUCTION

The logic state analyzer was described in Chap. 2. The logical first question with regard to a logic timing analyzer is, "How does it differ from a logic state analyzer?" The most important difference is that the timing analyzer has its own internal clock, and data is sampled on the active edge of this clock (Fig. 3-1). Since the internal clock operates asynchronously with respect to the system under test, the timing analyzer is called an asynchronous analyzer; the state analyzer is called a synchronous analyzer. This is illustrated in Fig. 3-2. The state analyzer provides the information that the system was in the state (1,0) on the first clock pulse, (0,1) on the second clock pulse, and so forth. The state analyzer only provides state and state-sequence information; unless a timer is added, no time information is provided. The timing analyzer, on the other hand, indicates that the top signal was low for T_L seconds and that the difference in time between the channels going low was T_D seconds. The timing analyzer does not resolve the state-sequence. For example, the system may have been in the state (0,0) for only one cycle of the external clock, or it may have been locked in that state for many cycles. That information is not provided directly by the timing analyzer.

The timing analyzer is directed toward observing the timing relationships between I/O signals or control lines and propagation delays between or across logic gates. The state analyzer is more useful in observing the state-sequence on digital system buses.

The timing analyzer display is a timing diagram that looks like a textbook presentation of an oscilloscope waveform. However, it is not an oscilloscope waveform. Data is sampled on every internal clock pulse, the analyzer deciding whether this data is greater or less than a threshold voltage and displaying the result as a logic one or zero. The display stays at that value until the next sample is taken. There are no analog values (such as

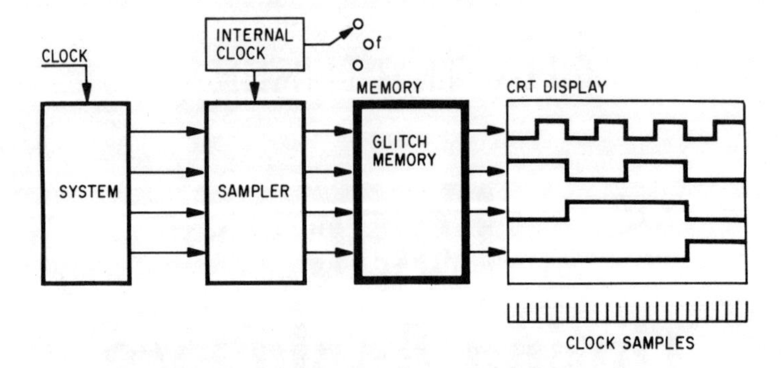

Fig. 3-1. The logic timing analyzer has an internal clock to asynchronously sample the external system. The results are displayed as a timing diagram that shows the logic state as a function of the timing analyzer's internal clock.

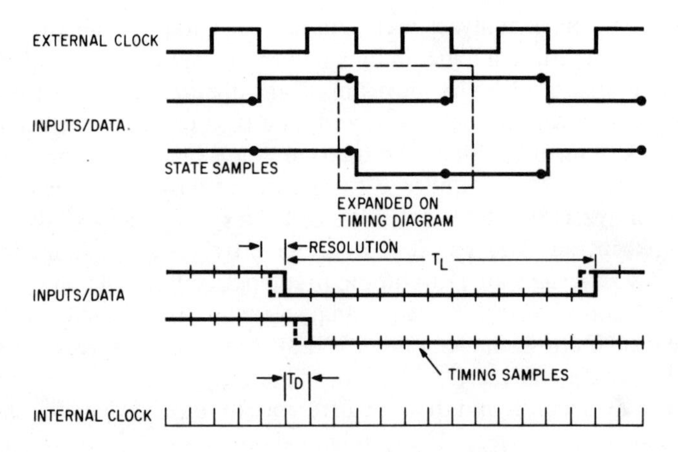

Fig. 3-2. The logic state analyzer interprets the logic state on the active transition of the external or system clock. A logic timing analyzer samples the data on the internal clock, resolving the inputs as shown. The first signal would be displayed low for T_L seconds while the difference in the two signals going low would be T_D seconds.

slow rises, ringing, or noise) that characterize time domain measurements; the results are either a high or a low.

3.2 TIMING ANALYZER RESOLUTION AND SKEW

The most important consideration when using an asynchronous instrument is to determine what resolution is adequate to make the measure-

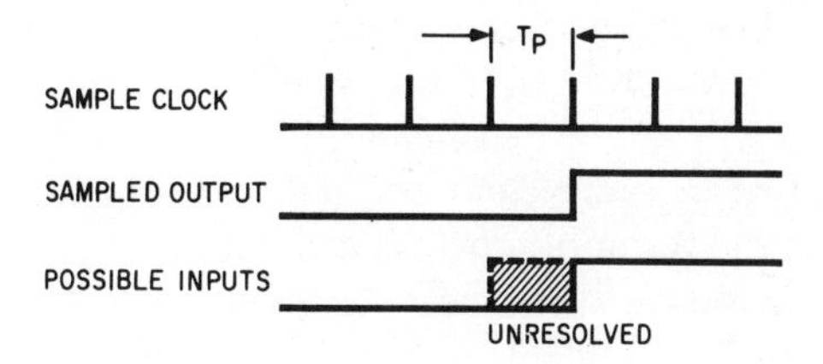

Fig. 3-3a. When a waveform is sampled, the signal may only be resolved to the clock period.

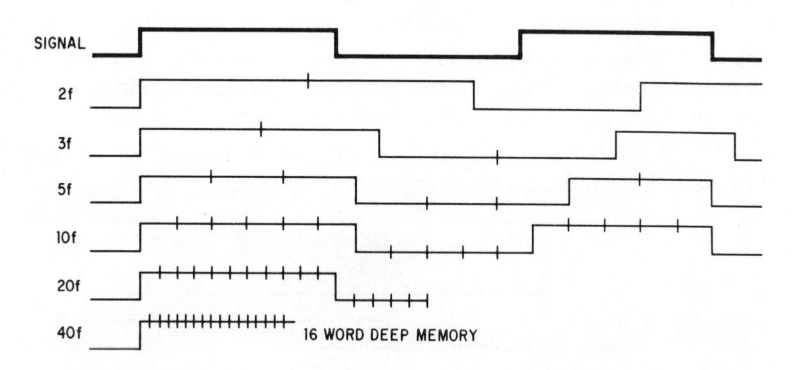

Fig. 3-3b. When sampled by a timing analyzer, the resolution of a square wave will depend upon the sampling frequency—the greater the frequency, the better the resolution, but the smaller the analyzer time window. For illustrative purposes, the memory has been assumed to be 16 bits deep. The first sampling pulse just catches the rising edge of the input signal. The pictures shown are the worst case.

ment in question. Fundamentally, the resolution cannot be better than the sample clock period. This is illustrated in Fig. 3-3a, where the unknown signal may have gone high at any time between two successive sample clocks. The resolution is T_P, the sample clock period. If a resolution of 0.1 μs is desired, a sample clock of 10 MHz must be used.

For the highest possible resolution, the clock frequency should be as high as possible. There are compromises to be considered; for a given memory capacity, a high frequency clock will only trace data over a narrow time span. Sample rates from five to ten times the data rate of the system under test normally provide a reasonable compromise between resolution and an adequate system timing overview. This is illustrated in Fig. 3-3b. Since most digital systems operate at data rates of only a few MHz maximum, a clock rate of 10 to 20 MHz will be adequate to resolve most timing problems. Narrow switching transients or glitches may be handled with glitch detection circuits.

From Fig. 3-3a it can be seen that it is possible to sample a signal right on its transition. However, if that edge is missed even by an infinitesimal amount, the signal will not be detected until one sample clock period later. When observing two or more channels, either channel could slip with respect to the other; the resolution between channels would be plus or minus the sample clock period ($\pm T_P$). This is shown in Fig. 3-4a.

In practice, owing to the physical dimensions of the probes, there will be substantial electrical delay between the probe tip inputs and the sampler circuit. Delay or set-up time delay on any channel will not cause problems, but the difference in delay between channels or skew does. In practice the skew may be as much as 10 ns. As shown in Fig. 3-4b, the skew may result in the signals being displayed in a different sequence than that in which they actually occurred. In general, high precision (parametric) measurements should not be expected with a timing analyzer; instead it should be reserved for functional measurements. If the timing between two signals is important, a timing analyzer with well-designed trigger logic may be used to resolve these two signals. This is discussed in Section 3.4.

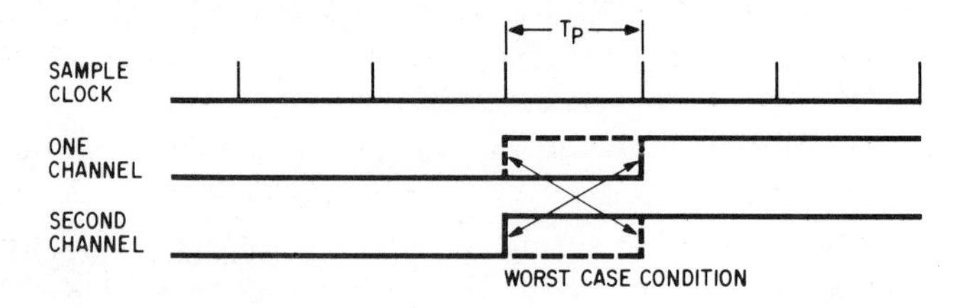

(a)

Fig. 3-4a. Worst case conditions illustrating the $\pm T_P$ resolution between channels.

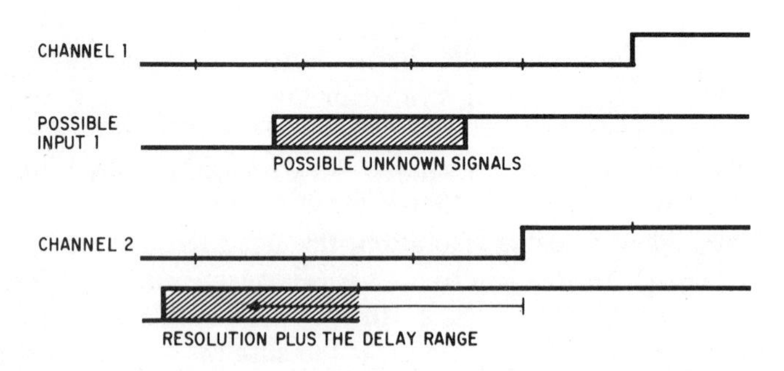

(b)

Fig. 3-4b. The diagrams show a timing analyzer display with two channels displaced by one sample clock pulse. When the resolution plus the delay is subtracted from the display, the unknown inputs could be in the shaded areas shown. As a result of variations in the delay (skew), the actual inputs may occur in a different sequence.

3.3 TEST SIGNAL CHARACTERISTICS

The discussion in Section 3.2 is based on the assumption that the signals under observation have sharp rise and fall times. Under these conditions there will be no timing errors due to differences in the threshold voltages of the system under test and the analyzer. However, practical devices do have finite rise and fall times, both of which can be influenced by analyzer loading. The clock to a microprocessor may have rise and fall times of up to 50 ns. For other microprocessor lines, these times may be considerably longer, especially if capacitively loaded. With these finite times, the signals under observation may lie within the voltage threshold limits for a considerable time, limiting the time resolution possible with a timing analyzer.

In circuits where the electrical dimensions are not small (or if high frequency probes are not supplied with the analyzer), transmission line effects become important. The output voltages reach their final value in a series of steps, each determined partly by the ratio of the transmission line characteristic impedance and circuit impedance. Some of these steps could easily lie within the voltage threshold limits, further reducing the analyzer accuracy. In a typical cable, the electrical signal will travel at 20 cm/ns, which can result in a 1 ns step for each 10 cm (4 in.) of cable (Fig. 3-5).

The uncertainties in the timing measurements due to the waveshapes can be reduced by carefully adjusting the threshold levels of the individual analyzer probes. Dual thresholds would assist with finite rise time signals—one level for rising edges, a second for falling edges. When high resolution measurements are really necessary, a true dual-beam oscilloscope should be used. This permits two of the signals in question to be observed. To window the oscilloscope in the required time frame, the logic analyzer should be used to trigger the oscilloscope.

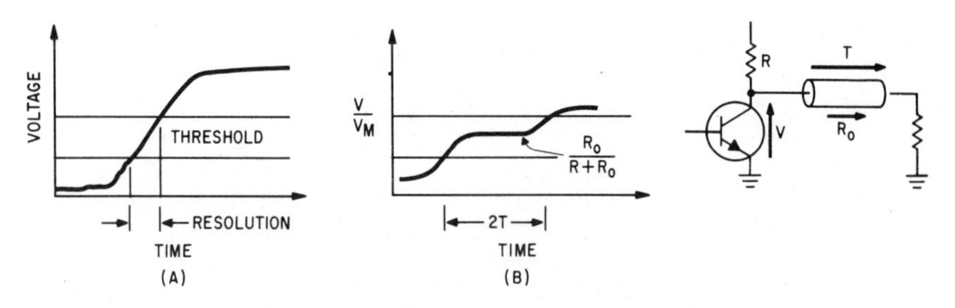

Fig. 3-5. (a) A typical circuit device will spend a finite time in the undefined regions between logic states. This time degrades the time resolution possible with a logic analyzer. (b) At high frequencies, the circuits take on transmission line characteristics. The output voltage will jump to its final value in a series of steps, any of which could lie in the indeterminate region, which reduces an analyzer's resolution of the system under observation.

In conclusion, the high resolution measurements that appear possible with high frequency asynchronous analyzers may not truly represent the system state due to the finite time the signals under observation spend in the undefined region about the logic threshold. The loading of the analyzer probes can also degrade the signal at very high frequency, further reducing the measurement accuracy.

3.4 ASYNCHRONOUS TRIGGERING OF THE TIMING ANALYZER

The timing analyzer is an asynchronous instrument. It is quite possible for the internal clock to sample the input data on a transient condition. Once sampled, this value becomes the assumed state until the next clock pulse. This state, while within the resolution limits discussed in Section 3.2, may not be a true representation of the system and could combine with other signals to satisfy the triggering conditions. In Fig. 3-6, the analyzer traps the transient state of (1,1). This is then stored in the memory and could satisfy the triggering conditions if the trigger logic is placed after the sampler, as in the state analyzer. One alternative is to include a time filter within the trigger logic. Then the trigger circuit is activated only if the

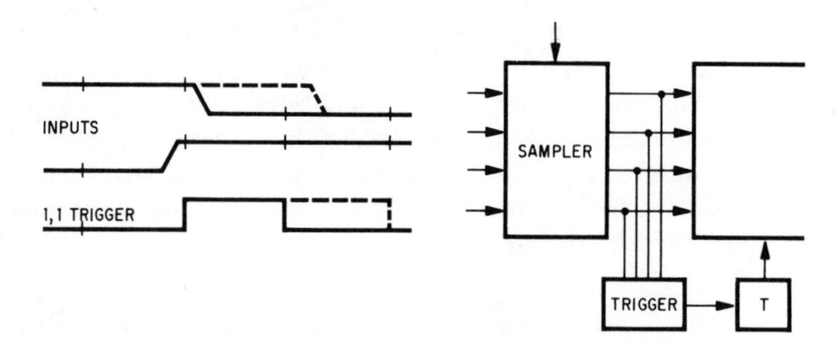

Fig. 3-6. On an asynchronous analyzer, sampling on a transient state of (1,1) will fix that data for the sample clock period. If this matches the trigger word, a post-sampling trigger circuit (as used in the state analyzer) would be triggered. If a time filter is added, the minimum time it may be set must be greater than one sample period. Then, if the trigger conditions are satisfied for only one sample (as shown), they are assumed to have been generated by a transient. If satisfied for greater than one sample period (shown by dotted lines), they may be assumed to be a valid state.

trigger conditions are met for greater than one sample period. This arrangement is a compromise solution—the sample period must be set short to ensure the analyzer triggers on some set of conditions, but the sample period must be relatively long if an overview of the activity following the trigger is to be captured.

A trigger time duration filter after the sampler operates only in integer multiples of the sampling period. To obtain time durations that are a fractional part of the sampling period, the trigger circuit should be placed in front of the sampler (Fig. 3-7). In this way the time duration filter can operate independently of the sampling period. For example (Fig. 3-8), the analyzer may be programmed to trigger on conditions that are met for less than 100 ns while taking samples at only a millisecond rate or less. Included in Fig. 3-7 are some of the timing analyzer controls. Notice that the delay can be either a time delay (from the internal clock) or a count delay (external clock). In addition, there will be an external output to provide a synchronizing signal when the trigger conditions are met.

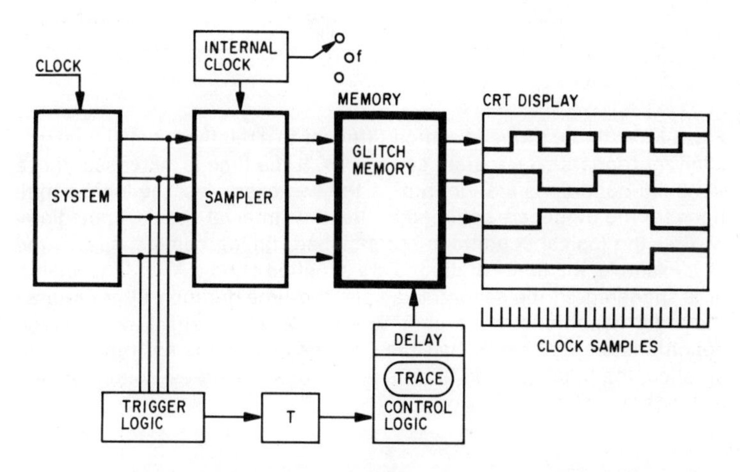

Fig. 3-7. To permit triggering of a timing analyzer independent of the sample clock, the trigger logic is placed before the sampler. The time duration filter (T) allows the operator to select the time that the trigger conditions must be satisfied to enable a trace.

In practice, the trigger logic would operate as follows: Once the trigger conditions state and time are satisfied, a latch is set. On the active edge of the next sample clock, the latch is tested; if the latch is set, a trace is enabled. Note that a trace is enabled at the clock edge, not when the trigger is satisfied. At the clock edge, the state of the system may have changed. Therefore, the actual trigger conditions will not be displayed on the screen at the display reference point. This causes no problem since the trigger indicator on the display indicates that the trigger conditions were satisfied during the last sample period.

Figure 3-9 shows some displays for various combinations of input data and the time duration filter. Since the trace commences at the conclusion of the sample period when the trigger conditions are satisfied, in some of the examples the state at the trigger point appears to conflict with that set (1,1) by the operator. Except for very narrow pulses, in these cases the trigger word will be seen as pretrigger data one cycle before the trigger point.

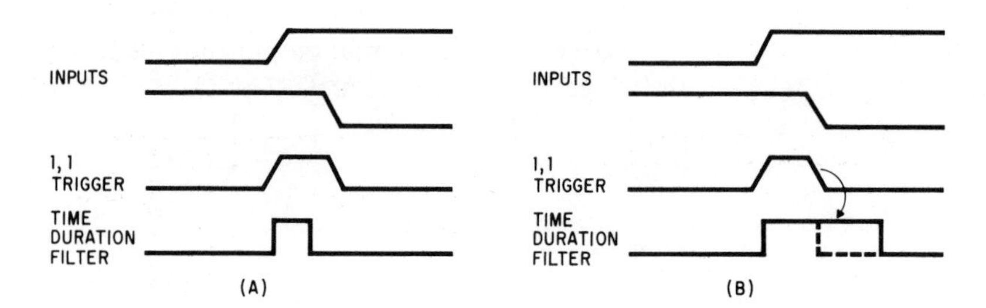

Fig. 3-8. With the trigger duration filter set to a relatively small time, the analyzer triggers on transient conditions. If the time is increased, these transient conditions are ignored. In the two examples, the logic conditions for the trigger are satisfied for the time interval shown. Immediately after the logical conditions are satisfied, timing commences. In the first example, the time conditions are satisfied at time A, and the analyzer is triggered. In the second example, the time duration filter requires the logic conditions to be continuously satisfied until time B. Logic conditions are not met in that time, so the analyzer is not triggered. In practice, the time duration filter is reset once the logical conditions are no longer satisfied.

When the trigger conditions are satisfied by a transient that lies entirely within the sample period, the trigger state may not be displayed at all (example 2 of Fig. 3-9d). If signal pulses of this duration are considered im-

Fig. 3-9. The trigger time duration filter allows the operator to select the time the input conditions must be satisfied to enable a trace. The trace is enabled at the next sampling point after the triggering conditions were satisfied. The examples assume a two-channel timing analyzer with the waveforms shown. The trigger must satisfy both the state and time conditions. Programmed to recognize a (1,1) trigger, the state conditions are satisfied over the time interval shown shaded. Once the state conditions are satisfied, the timing commences. With the time duration filter set to a relatively short time (example b), the analyzer traces from the next clock sample.

Increasing the time requirements delays the trace (examples c and d). Once the trigger conditions are satisfied, a trace commences at

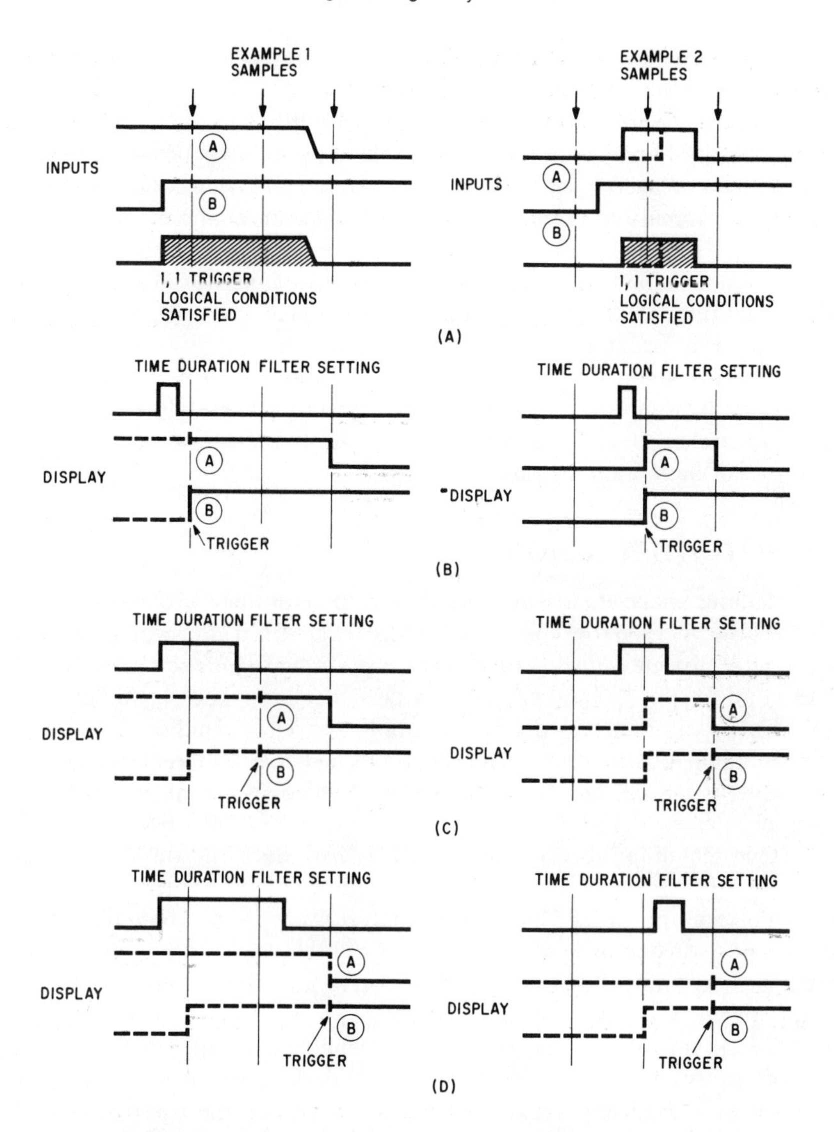

(Continued)
the conclusion of that sample period. Between satisfying the trigger requirements and the next sample, the inputs may change. This is illustrated in (c) right and (d) left where the trigger is the state (1,1). However, the data has changed to the state (0,1) by the clock sample, and it is this data that is displayed at the trigger point on the screen. The state (1,1) would usually appear as pretrigger data, except in the case shown on the right in (d) in which the state (1,1) occurs entirely within one sample period. In this example the trigger word is never displayed unless the timing analyzer has glitch detection circuits.

portant, the operator should use special glitch circuits to display these narrow transient states as glitches (see Section 3.5).

The trigger circuits are often used to find information without going to the display. For example, consider the case of two non-overlapping clocks. If the trigger is set to the state (1,1) and the trigger time duration filter to the minimum possible (typically 15 ns), an analyzer indicates no trigger for overlaps less than 15 ns. If the overlap is greater than 15 ns, a trace will be enabled showing the consequences of the overlap. This same time resolution on the display could only be achieved with a 200 MHz timing analyzer with no more than 5 ns of skew.

In many applications, the triggering capability may be the most crucial requirement on an analyzer. The more precisely the analyzer can focus in on a problem, the less dependent it is on other features such as large memories or high sampling rates.

3.5 GLITCH DETECTION

Timing analyzers are used to observe time-domain problems, one of which is the very narrow spike or glitch. Any circuit while switching draws substantial current, which in turn may cause voltage drops across any resistance in power lines. Good engineering design calls for the placing of small (.01 μF) capacitors across the power supply at every second or third circuit chip to reduce potential problems. Not all glitches will be removed by this technique; it is necessary to observe the various nodes and display potential glitch problems.

One technique to observe a glitch is to reduce the timing interval. However, this increases the memory capacity required for the same overview. For example, a 20 MHz timing analyzer is quite adequate to observe microprocessor operations. To detect 5 ns glitches on the microprocessor lines, the clock must be increased to 200 MHz, requiring a tenfold increase in both the memory speed and capacity.

To circumvent the use of high frequency clocks and increased high speed memory, most timing analyzers have special glitch detection circuits on all input lines. These circuits, when enabled, detect these narrow spikes. A simple form of glitch detector is the pulse stretcher or latch that stretches a narrow pulse to the point at which it is detected as a minimum width pulse. With this type of instrument, two observations of the line under test are necessary, one with the latch circuits enabled and a second observation with the latch circuits disabled. Any minimum width pulses that occur with the latch enabled and disappear when the latch is disabled are in fact glitches, i.e., pulses with a time duration less than the sample period.

A disadvantage of the latch detectors is that a very common source of problems goes undetected, namely, the glitch on the leading or tailing edge of a standard pulse (Fig. 3-10). A better form of glitch detection is provided

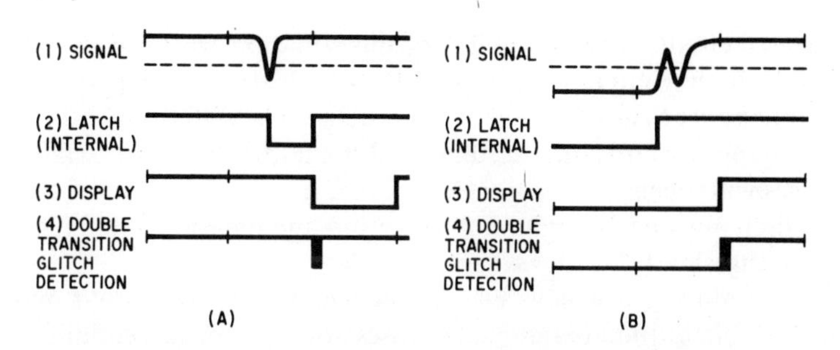

Fig. 3-10. A latch circuit detects a transition across the threshold voltage. If at the end of the sample window the state has not changed, the transition is interpreted as a glitch and displayed as a minimum width pulse (a3). If the state did change, the transition is ignored and the new state is displayed. Glitches on pulses will be missed using this technique (b3). The special double-transition glitch detection circuits will display the glitch as an intensified spike (a4 and b4).

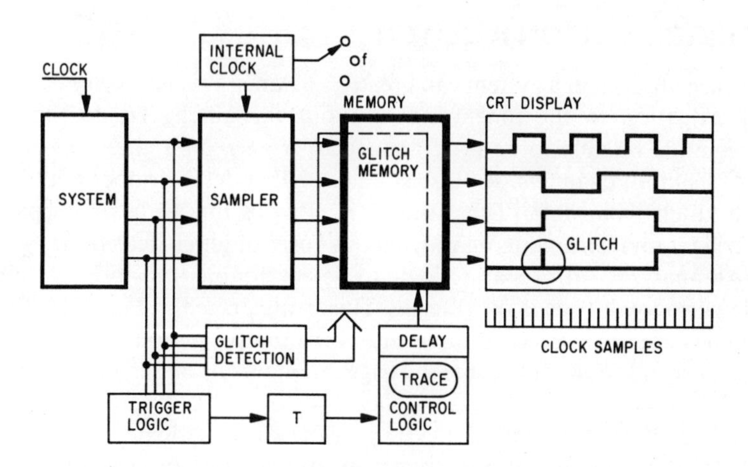

Fig. 3-11. To capture glitches, special circuits are added to each input line. Any double transition within the sample period is captured as a glitch and stored in a second memory. When the glitch display is enabled, the glitch is displayed as an intensified spike on screen.

by the use of high speed logic circuits that detect any double transition across the input threshold level within one sample period. The presence of this double transition is stored in a second memory and is superimposed on the timing diagram as an intensified spike (Fig. 3-11). These circuits detect glitches on the edge of pulses, and the display shows the pulse with an intensified edge (Fig. 3-10). Only when the glitch exactly coincides with the asynchronous clock (Fig. 3-12) will these special circuits fail to display a glitch; it will be displayed as a minimum width pulse, as would be the case with the latch circuit. The probability of this situation arising is given by the ratio of the glitch width to the sampling period. The sampling period, therefore, should be set to as great a width as is consistent with the measurement. If the sampling period is increased beyond the duration of any data pulses, these pulses will themselves be traced as glitches.

A glitch must be of a minimum duration and have an amplitude in excess of the threshold (i.e., overdrive) in order to be detected. Many digital systems have glitches at some or all of their nodes. These may or may not present a problem; the operator must assess the system susceptibility. The glitch detection and trigger circuits in Fig. 3-11 are in parallel with the sampling circuits, so each will have its own specifications. For example, the sampling circuit requires the signal to be stable before the active clock edge (set-up) and possibly after the clock (hold). The trigger logic requires selection of the time duration filter, while the glitch circuits require the glitch to have a minimum duration. There are no set-up and hold times on the glitch circuits.

3.6 TRIGGERING ON A GLITCH

Since glitches in a system can create problems, it is necessary to direct the investigation to the time window about the glitch. To do this, the analyzer must be able to be programmed to trigger on a glitch on one or more of its input channels. A pulse stretcher glitch detector does not distinguish a glitch from data. Therefore, it is not possible to have a separate glitch trigger on instruments employing this form of glitch detection.

An analyzer with separate logic to detect double transitions within a sample period will trigger on glitches. This is illustrated in Fig. 3-13. Since the glitch is not recognized until the end of the sample period, the states following those at the glitch become the trigger conditions on screen. As shown in Fig. 3-13, in the Trigger Starts Display mode one set of negative time data is displayed. This is the data at the time of the glitch. A logic analyzer may not provide an output pulse to trigger an oscilloscope on a glitch since a glitch is not interpreted until the end of a sample period. By that time it would be missed by an oscilloscope.

In many systems glitches occur frequently. Only some of these cause any problems, and it is these that should be isolated for closer examination. The states at which problems are likely to arise should be defined in the trigger conditions along with a glitch; i.e., the analyzer must be programmed to trigger on a given state *and* a glitch on any defined input. This is illustrated in Fig. 3-14, where the state conditions plus a glitch on line 1 are satisfied in the one sample period.

In a timing analyzer, if the state conditions are satisfied at any time during the sample period, this is "remembered" until the end of that period. Similarly, a glitch is "remembered," and at the end of the period the analyzer tests whether the total triggering conditions are met. In Fig. 3-

14, while the second glitch and the (0,0) state conditions do not occur concurrently, they do occur in the one sample period. Hence, the triggering conditions are met.

If the trigger state conditions were changed to (0,1), the trigger conditions would not be satisfied until a time after line 2 goes to state 1. This time is determined by the trigger window. If the time period is sufficiently small,

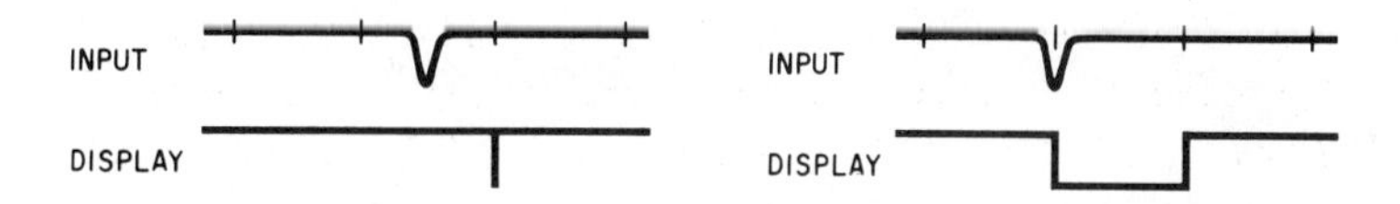

Fig. 3-12. Should the sample instance coincide with the glitch, the glitch will be displayed as a minimum width pulse.

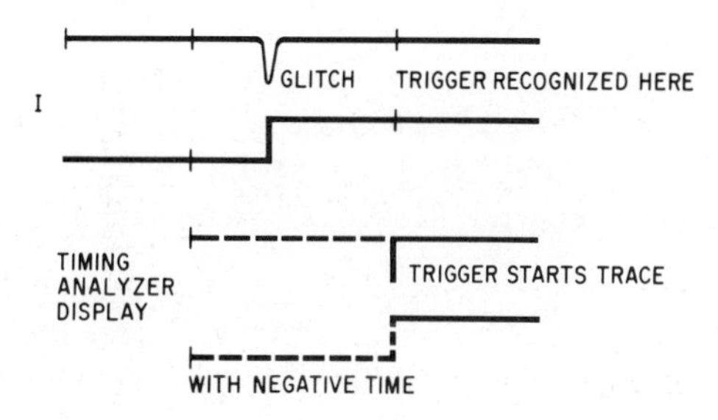

Fig. 3-13. A glitch is not recognized until the end of the sampling period in which it occurred. Hence, the normal Trigger Starts Display mode would not indicate conditions at the glitch. By including at least one bit of negative time data, the transitions that caused the glitch are displayed.

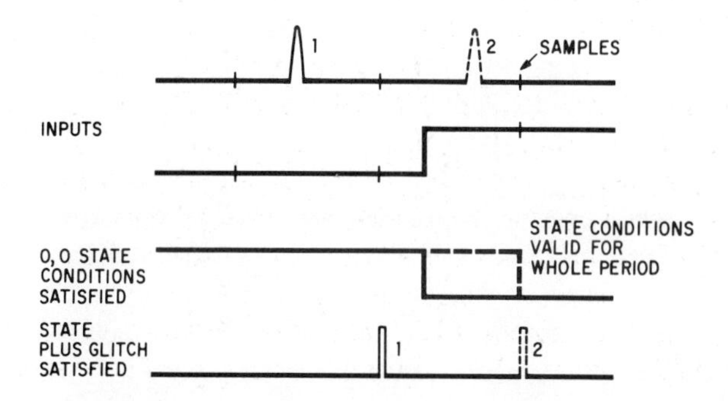

Fig. 3-14. The state and glitch conditions are satisfied within the sample period, and the analyzer is triggered. Since the analyzer only tests at the end of each sample period, a glitch in position 2 would also satisfy trigger requirements.

the state conditions are satisfied within the sample period and the analyzer would be triggered. *Note:* Once the state conditions are satisfied, the analyzer does not start retiming at the beginning of each sample period.

3.7 INTERACTIVE STATE AND TIMING ANALYSIS

Both timing and state analyzers have external outputs to provide synchronizing signals on pattern recognition. Input sockets are also provided to allow external signals to either arm or trigger the analyzer. Two analyzers, a timing analyzer and a state analyzer, could be interconnected and operated in one of the following modes:

asynchronous	arms/triggers	synchronous
synchronous	arms/triggers	asynchronous

Rather than use two separate instruments, an analyzer that combines both state and timing functions could be used. In addition to convenience, more extensive measurements will be available with a single instrument since it will have been designed as an integral unit. One example of the interaction possible with a combined instrument (the HP Model 1615A) is discussed in the *Hewlett-Packard Journal*, February 1978, in the article "Interactive Logic State and Timing Analyzers for Tracking Down Problems in Digital Systems" by John A. Scharrer, Robert G. Wickliff, Jr., and William D. Martin:

> The example concerns a microprocessor system under development that had a small keypad for data entry and control. It had been observed that the system detected a key-down condition and serviced the key when in fact no key had been pressed. To track down this problem, Model 1615A, set up in the timing mode, was connected to the microprocessor's interrupt line and set to trigger on a high on this line. Model 1615A then displayed interrupt pulses of normal duration on this line when none should have occurred. However, no glitches were detected.
>
> Additional logic timing analyzer inputs were then connected to the inputs to the interrupt-request generator, a monostable multivibrator. Model 1615A showed that a glitch occurred on one of these inputs.
>
> The next step was to find out what was happening in the system when the glitch occurred. The state probes of Model 1615A were connected to the microprocessor's address bus and the analyzer was switched to dual state and timing operation. The trigger was changed to start the timing trace on the glitch of the interrupt-request generator's input line, and the timing analyzer part of the instrument was used to end data capture by the state analyzer part. The microprocessor states leading up to the glitch were thus captured for display. Repeated tracings made in this mode revealed that the micro-

processor was always executing the same instructions when the glitch occurred.

The listing of the microprocessor code showed that the instruction being executed when the glitch occurred was "read I/O port 200." The I/O read line and the chip-select input to port 200 were then connected to the timing machine. The resulting timing display revealed the source of the problem: the falling edge of the I/O read pulse coincided with the glitch.

Examination of the circuit board revealed that these two signals ran side by side for some distance. Rerouting one of them to eliminate the capacitive coupling between lines solved the problem.

In the example just quoted, the timing portion of the analyzer triggered the state in a trigger ends trace mode. The two-decade BCD counter discussed in Chap. 2 is another example for which a dual instrument would be ideal. In that case, the state portion would trigger the timing on the state 59. The timing portion would monitor all the control lines and simultaneously display the control signals, one of which may have caused the counter to skip states 60 through 69. With the interactive state/timing analyzer, all the state-time information is captured in one shot, unlike the state analyzer/oscilloscope combination that requires many passes.

3.8 CONCLUSION

The timing analyzer must satisfy the following design criteria:

1. The instrument must be multinodal in order to monitor transition on several lines simultaneously.
2. The analyzer must have adequate resolution.
3. The trigger or trace point duration must be selectable.
4. The analyzer must be able to reliably detect and uniquely display glitches.
5. A trigger activated by a glitch must also be available.
6. To allow an expanded display window to be positioned away from the trigger point, a timing analyzer must have provision for delaying in units of time or states.

Many problems encountered in a digital system may be identified using a variety of instruments and techniques. Problems that require asynchronous instruments and techniques for solutions include the observation of multichannel phenomenon (where the timing is critical, especially when the events cannot be easily repeated or occur in negative time before the trigger) and the capturing, displaying, and triggering on glitches. These problems often arise on the control lines of processor systems and on the interface between the processor and the peripheral devices.

CHAPTER FOUR

Logic Analyzers and the Standard I/O Buses

4.1 STANDARD INSTRUMENTATION BUS IEEE-488

The IEEE-488 instrumentation bus consists of 16 lines of known parameters that permit instruments to interact with one another. The 16 lines are in three sets: five lines provide interface management; three lines are used for the handshake or data byte transfer control; and the remaining eight lines carry general data (Fig. 4-1).

The three interface signal lines are used to effect the transfer of each byte of data on the bidirectional data lines from an addressed talker to all addressed listeners:

(1) DAV (data valid) indicates the condition (availability and validity) of information on the Data I/O (DIO) signal lines.
(2) NRFD (not ready for data) indicates the condition of readiness of device(s) to accept data.
(3) NDAC (not data accepted) indicates the condition of acceptance of data by device(s).

The DAV, NRFD, and NDAC signal lines operate in what is called a three-wire interlocked handshake process to transfer each data byte across the interface. This is illustrated in Fig. 4-2.

The handshake sequence is entered with the listener-controlled lines NRFD and NDAC both low. Since the talker will not have valid data, the DAV line will be released and will be pulled high by the pull-up resistor. As each listener becomes ready to receive data, it releases the not ready for data line (NRFD). When all listeners have released the NRFD line, the pull-up resistors will pull it high. Once the talker has new data, it signals new data valid by pulling the DAV line low. The listeners respond by pulling their NRFD line low. As the listeners actually read or accept data, they release the not data accepted (NDAC) line. When all listeners have accepted the data, the NDAC line goes high. The talker acknowledges by releasing the DAV line, and the listeners complete the handshake by pulling the NDAC

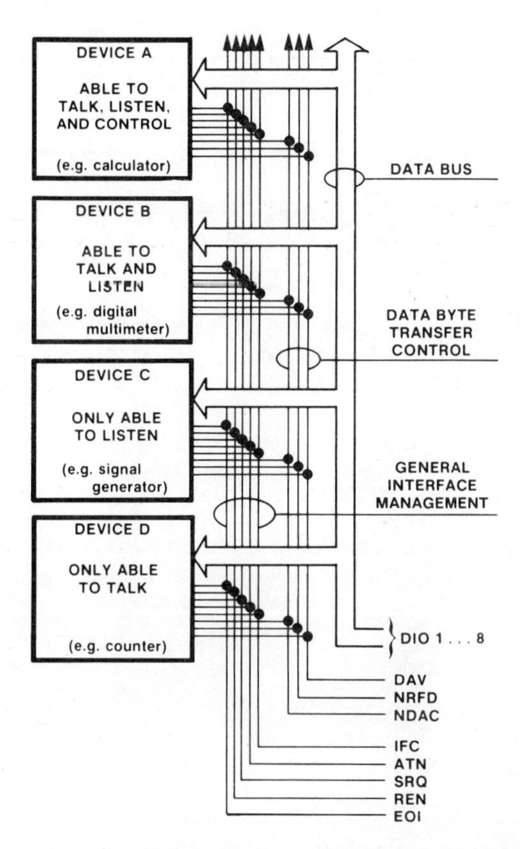

Fig. 4-1. Interface capabilities and IEEE-488 bus structure.

line low. A legal handshake must proceed in the sequence shown in Fig. 4-2. The NRFD and NDAC lines may never be high together.

Data transfer on the interface bus may be monitored with a logic state analyzer. Since the bus operates in negative logic, the analyzer format is set to negative logic. The three handshake and five management lines normally are displayed in binary, while the display of the eight data lines should be in a convenient number base. Either edge of the DAV control line, the falling edge of NRFD, or the rising edge of NDAC may be used to clock data into the analyzer.

If the data transfer breaks down, the control lines can be examined for breaches of the bus protocol with a timing analyzer. For more complete monitoring of the instrumentation bus, special circuits (Fig. 4-3) may be manufactured. These special circuits resolve the conflicting requirements of monitoring relatively long cycle times with high resolution at the transitions, circumstances in which a timing analyzer has limitations. For each data transfer, the results of testing are combined into one signal, the normal

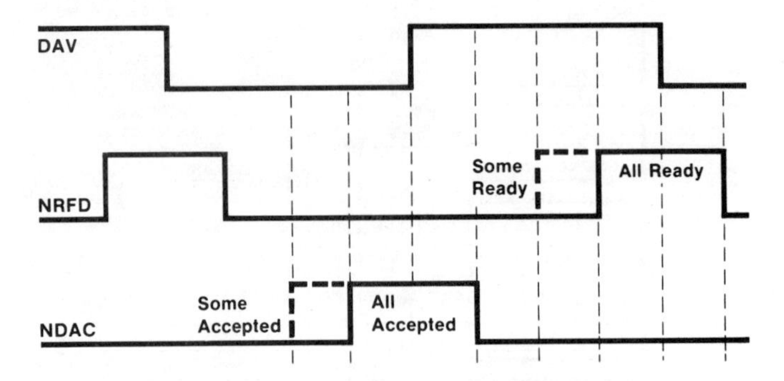

(a)

(b)

Fig. 4-2. (a) Handshake waveforms for the IEEE-488 instrumentation bus. (b) Handshake line sequences. All states are in negative logic.

handshake line from the test circuit or probe. With the special circuit of Fig. 4-3, the handshake timing may be confirmed to a resolution compatible with the propagation delays and set-up times of the devices used in the circuit. These delays typically amount to 25 ns, the same resolution as a single channel 40 MHz timing analyzer. *Note:* a 40 MHz timing analyzer would require a memory capacity of 160 words to examine one handshake operation functioning at 250k bytes/s. By contrast, a state analyzer with the special probe adjusts to the data rate and requires only one memory location for each data transfer operation. Further, a bad handshake is readily detected and could be used to trigger the analyzer or an external oscilloscope.

A typical listing for a logic analyzer monitoring the interface bus with a preprocessor (Fig. 4-3) is shown in Table 4-1. In the listing, the logic an-

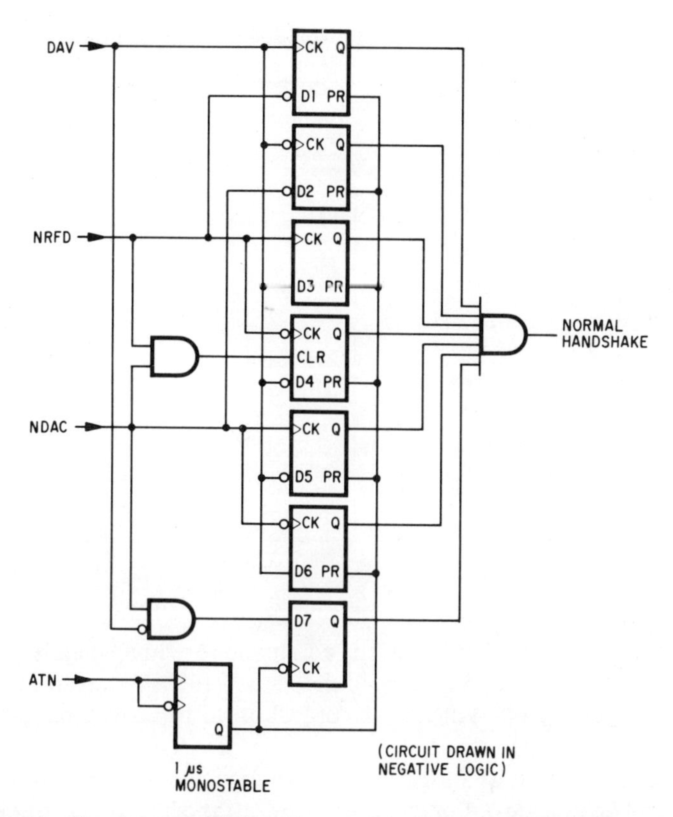

Fig. 4-3. Circuit to test IEEE-488 bus protocol. Any invalid tests leave the normal handshake line at a logic zero (high). (i) One microsecond after a transition of the ATN line (after the controller either takes over or passes control of the bus), D7 tests that the initialization was completed correctly, i.e., DAV high and NDAC low. (ii) If the NDAC and NRFD lines are ever high together (logic zero), the clear line of D4 will cause the normal handshake line to go high. (iii) On each data transfer, the handshake lines are tested to determine if the data transfer proceeds in the normal sequence as defined in Fig. 4-2b. For example, when DAV goes to a logic one, D1 tests that NRFD is at logic zero. On the other edge of DAV, NDAC is checked for a logic zero by D2.

alyzer has been set 14 bits wide with the 8 bits that monitor the data lines (bits 0–7) formatted in hexadecimal. The data could also be translated to ASCII characters. In the example, the controller on the interface bus

(1) Commands all devices to ignore any data that is on the DIO lines (when ATN is high or logic 0)
(2) Commands device 21 to talk
(3) Commands device 15 to listen

Table 4-1. Typical logic analyzer listing of IEEE-488 interface bus activity.

Word	LRISEA HEFROT SNCQIN	Data Hex	Data ASCII	Comments
0	110001	3F	?	All devices unlisten
1	110001	55	U	Device 21_{10} Talk
2	110001	2F	/	Device 15_{10} Listen
3	110000	57	W	
4	110000	31	1	
5	110000	36	6	
6	110000	42	B	
7	110000	31	1	
8	110000	50	P	
9	110000	31	1	
10	110000	43	C	
11	110000	32	2	
12	110000	4D	M	
13	110000	31	1	
14	110000	0D	Car. Ret	
15	110000	0A	Line Feed	

As the ATN line is released, the commands are immediately executed. Device 21 talks to device 15, sending the data W16B1P1 and so forth, with each transfer taking place under the control of the three-wire handshake. If the handshake is interpreted as legal by the preprocessor logic, the legal handshake line will be at a logic 1. However, if any handshake is not legal, this line will be at logic 0. For example, if one of the line drivers of device 15 were faulty, both the NRFD and NDAC lines would be high (logic 0) together at the same stage in each data transfer. The preprocessor would detect the illegal handshake and display it as a logic zero on bit 14 of the logic analyzer. By triggering on an illegal handshake, the operator would be able to narrow subsequent investigations to the problem areas.

4.2 MONITORING SERIAL DATA BUSES

Introduction

A logic state analyzer examines data on a multichannel parallel bus and provides a functional display of the state sequence. In many communication systems, all the data lines are combined into one (half-duplex system) or two (full-duplex) lines, and the information is transmitted serially on these lines. A typical serial communication link is the RS-232C illustrated in Fig. 4-4.

The operation of the RS-232C interface bus is as follows:

(1) Initially the data terminal equipment (DTE) places the modem into the data mode by placing a signal on the line, data terminal ready (DTR). While in the data mode and connected to the telephone line, the

modem acknowledges by placing a signal on data set ready (DSR). Should DTR ever go off, the modem will disconnect from the telephone line at the end of the call.

(2) When the receive circuits detect a carrier from a distant modem, the carrier detector (CD) goes on. Data will be received some time later on the received data (RX) line.

(3) The terminal equipment would be expected to reply. To do so, it first turns on the request to send (RTS) line. When ready, the modem replies via the clear to send (CTS) line. Once the CTS is on, data is transmitted over the transmit data (TX) line. In the Bell 103A system shown, the RTS is not used; the carrier detector and clear to send carry simultaneous signals.

The system shown is an asynchronous system; the terminal must reinsert a clock into the data stream received from the modem, while the modem must insert a clock into the transmitted data. If the modem was of the synchronous type, it would contain two clocks—one for received data and one for transmitted data (pins 15 and 17). While not usual, a signal to synchronize the serial data could be placed on one of the unassigned pins.

Any instrument designed to monitor a serial bus such as the RS-232C must have the following capabilities:

(1) Monitor synchronous data
 (a) With separate sync control

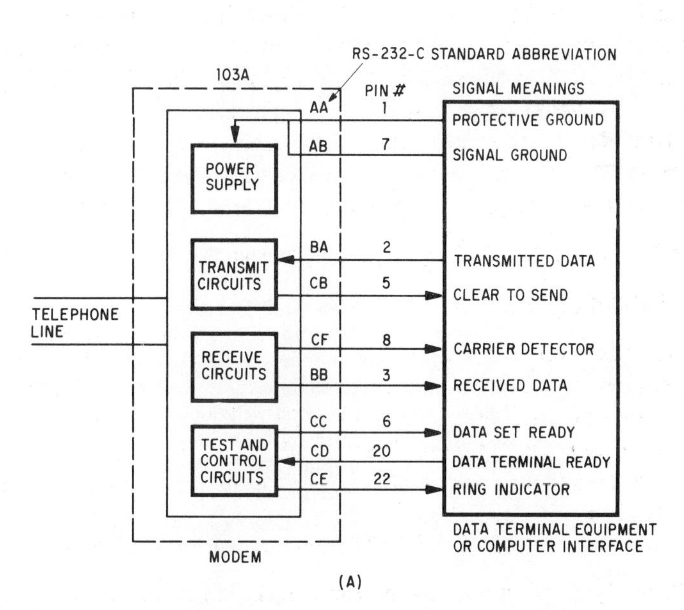

Fig. 4-4. Typical RS-232C serial communication link. (a) Bell 103A simplified interface block diagram.

(b)Without separate sync control
(2) Monitor asynchronous data
(3) Measure control parameters, e.g., timing

Monitoring Synchronous Serial Data Buses

From an operational standpoint, the simplest serial bus format will consist of three lines: one line contains a clock; the second, data; and the third, a synchronizing pulse. A serial logic analyzer could be constructed using a standard state analyzer with a serial-to-parallel converter placed on the input as shown in Fig. 4-5. As each word is packed into parallel format, it is clocked into the logic analyzer. Alternatively, the two units could be constructed as one complete serial unit. When constructed as a single unit, the instrument may be designed to monitor those functions unique to serial data streams rather than be limited to the parallel analyzer features. Since many serial buses are full-duplex, some of the circuits of Fig. 4-5 would be

Signal Direction		Pin		
Terminal	Modem	Number	Circuit	Description
		1	AA	Protective Ground
		2	BA	Transmitted Data
		3	BB	Received Data
		4	CA	Request to Send
		5	CB	Clear to Send
		6	CC	Data Set Ready
		7	AB	Signal Ground (Common Return)
		8	CF	Received Line Signal Detector
		9	—	(Reserved for Data Set Testing)
		10	—	(Reserved for Data Set Testing)
		11	—	Unassigned
		12	SCF	Secondary Received Line Signal Detector
		13	SCB	Secondary Clear to Send
		14	SBA	Secondary Transmitted Data
		15	DB	Transmission Signal Element Timing (DCE Source)
		16	SBB	Secondary Received Data
		17	DD	Receiver Signal Element Timing (DCE Source)
		18		Unassigned
		19	SCA	Secondary Request to Send
		20	CD	Data Terminal Ready
		21	CG	Signal Quality Detector
		22	CE	Ring Indicator
		23	CH/CI	Data Signal Rate Selector (DTE/DCE Source)
		24	DA	Transmit Signal Element Timing (DTE Source)
		25		Unassigned

Fig. 4-4 *(cont.)*. (b) EIA RS-232C interface connector pin assignments.

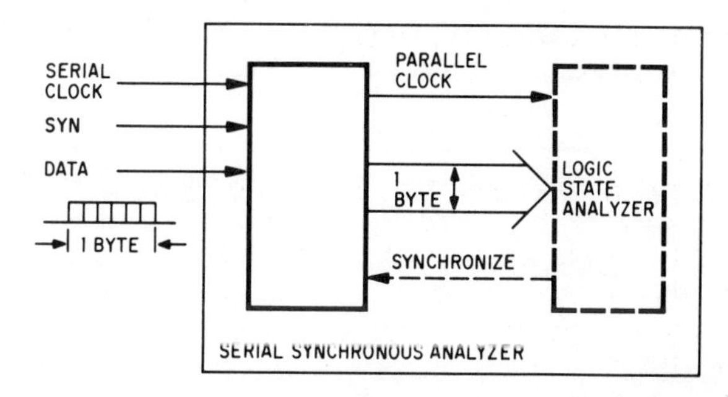

Fig. 4-5. The serial-to-parallel converter takes the serial data and formats it into parallel form, providing a clock for each new byte of parallel data. The parallel data is then traced with a logic state analyzer. The serial-to-parallel converter has controls that define the position, width, and number of data bytes within the serial sequence. The converter and an analyzer can be combined as one to form a serial logic analyzer.

duplicated, e.g., for collection of TX and RX data. The transmitted and received data would then be interleaved on screen to show the time relationship. The two sets of data would be distinguished, for example, by placing one in inverse video. A dedicated serial analyzer displays the data in a communication language such as ASCII or EBCDIC.

The description of the controls contained in the serial-to-parallel converter section are best explained with the aid of Fig. 4-6. This figure shows the waveforms associated with a disc memory. The system is synchronous; with each clock pulse there is one new bit of data. There is a signal (SOD) that references the starting point of all messages. To pack the data into parallel form, the converter is programmed to delay 15 bits or clock pulses after the synchronizing pulse and then generate or pack the serial data into parallel words or bytes of 16 bits each. These two parameters are set on the converter controls. The state analyzer portion is set to a word width of 16 bits.

Some refinements are possible. For example, the converter has a display format control that allows the first serial bit to be treated as either the most significant bit (MSB) or least significant bit (LSB). As another example, to permit tracing of only words 1 and 2 following each sync pulse, an additional control (the bytes/sync control) can be set to 2. The serial-to-parallel converter would then only output two words per sync pulse.

Most synchronous systems do not have the third line containing the synchronizing pulse; the serial data ripples across the parallel outputs of the serial-to-parallel converter at the same rate as the serial clock. When the state analyzer recognizes a bit pattern, it outputs a signal to synchronize the serial-to-parallel converter. The converter then switches modes and only outputs parallel data in the format set with the front panel controls. In this mode, the synchronizing pattern must be unique to avoid triggering on a

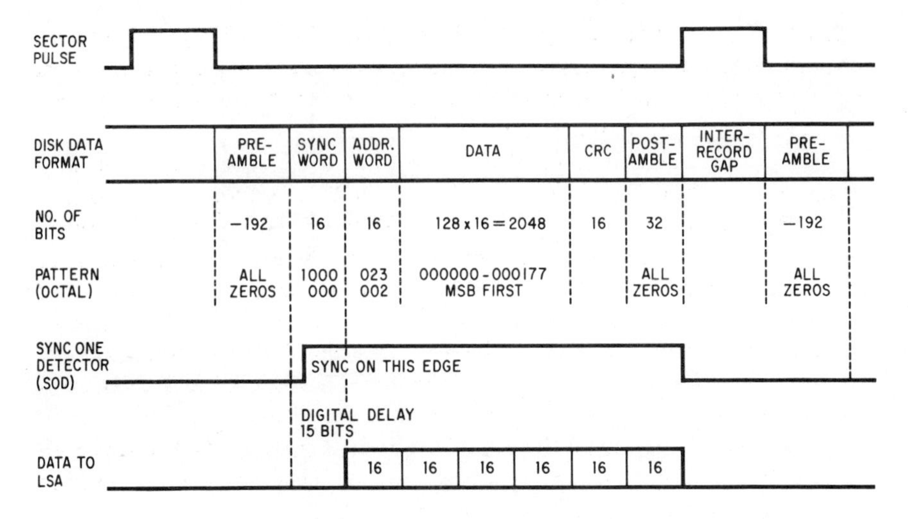

Fig. 4-6. In the edge sync mode, the converter permits the display of selected data by synchronizing on the leading edge of the Sync One Detector waveform and delaying past the disc preamble into the address and data stream. In this example, the delay after sync is set to 15 bits, and the bits per byte is set to 16. If the address word were not required in the display, the delay after sync would be set to 31.

pattern composed of the final bits of one byte and the leading bits of the next byte.

When idling, the transmitter often transmits the hexadecimal word 16_{16}, which is recognized as the ASCII command SYN (synchronize). The receivers, including the serial logic analyzer, remain synchronized by detecting the SYN character. An analyzer designed for serial operation should have a suppress mode that removes any repetitive character such as SYN from the trace.

One disadvantage of the two-unit serial analyzer shown in Fig. 4-5 is that two trigger signals may be necessary, one to provide a synchronizing pulse to the serial-to-parallel converter and a second pulse to provide the reference to window the trace. Further, with serial data it is often necessary to trigger on a sequence of characters that occur on either the transmit or receive half of a full-duplex system. These limitations may be overcome in part with intelligent use of the state analyzer; however, in general, a serial analyzer that has triggering capabilities compatible with the requirements dictated by the serial data is to be preferred.

Monitoring Asynchronous Serial Data Buses

Synchronous serial data has a clock that defines every new bit of information. There may be an additional line that provides a synchronizing signal to align a serial analyzer with the serial data. With asynchronous serial transmissions, neither of these signals is available. The detector must reinsert the clock, and it must synchronize with the start bits now included in every byte transmitted over the bus.

In operation, the asynchronous serial analyzer operates like a universal asynchronous receiver transmitter (UART). A front panel control sets an internal clock to operate at 16 times the serial bit rate. Once synchronized, every 16th clock will be used by the analyzer to sample and, hence, define the bit on the serial bus. The serial data format includes at least one stop bit at the conclusion of each transmitted byte. The signal is high for the stop bit and remains high until the next data byte. To start each new byte, the bus goes low to give a start bit. The receiver (and asynchronous serial analyzer) detects the high to low transition, waits eight clock pulses, and synchronizes on the center of the start bit (Fig. 4-7). Every 16th clock pulse will now define the center of the data bit. After a preset number of bits, the bus will go high for at least one stop bit.

With an asynchronous serial analyzer, the operator must define the bit rate, the number of data bits, and the number of stop bits. Often the data will be in 8-bit ASCII with the eighth bit used as a parity check. Some serial analyzers will have the capability of triggering on a parity error. In that case, the operator must define the parity.

Monitoring Serial Bus Control Lines

Control lines of any serial bus operate similar to those of the RS-232C discussed in the introduction to Section 4.2. The types of measurements that need to be made on these lines are timing in nature; e.g., how long is it between the RTS (request to send) and CTS (clear to send) signals? A serial analyzer indicates activity on any of the control buses and can be programmed to trigger on specified time intervals between control signals. Displays are in one of the conventional state analyzer modes, Trigger Starts/Ends Display or Count Triggers modes.

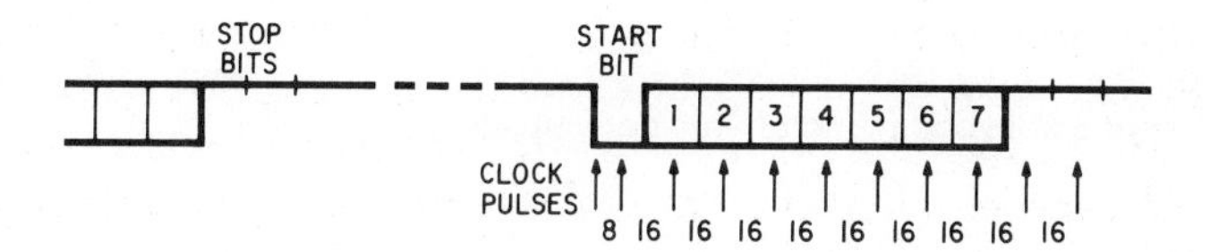

Fig. 4-7. Typical asynchronous serial waveforms. Between bytes the bus will idle high. Upon receipt of a low, the internal logic commences timing. If the bus is still low eight clock pulses later, the receiver assumes it is a start bit and reads off the data after every 16th clock pulse. In the example shown, the receiver would be programmed in a 7-bit mode. After the preset number of stop bits, the receiver waits for the next start pulse.

Table 4-2. Model 1602A Option 001 device dependent commands.

Measurement Data Format

B1	sets	Hexadecimal	P1	sets	Positive logic polarity
B2	sets	Decimal	P2	sets	Negative logic polarity
B3	sets	Octal	C1	sets	Positive clock edge
B4	sets	Binary	C2	sets	Negative clock edge
Wx.	sets	word width = x; $2 \leq x \leq 16$*			
Fx	sets	coded subfield width = x; $2 \leq x \leq$ word width*			

*See word width rules in 1602A Operating and Service Manual.

Trace Specifications

M1.	sets	Start Trace on Trigger + Delay
M2.	sets	End Trace on Trigger + Delay
Dx	sets	Delay = x; $0 \leq x \leq 65535$
Tx	sets	Trigger = x ; x must fit current format exactly
Ex	sets	Delay by Trigger Events = x; $0 \leq x \leq 65535$

Execute

R. .... causes Trace execution and configures 1602A to transmit unformatted data as in U. Aborts any previous Trace in progress.

Z. .... causes Trace Trigger Events (TRACE E) execution and configures 1602A to transmit unformatted data as in U. Aborts any previous Trace in progress.

H. .... halts any Trace in progress.

Output

Nx. .... configures 1602A to transmit formatted data in memory Word Number = x; $0 \leq x \leq 63$ (at conclusion of Trace)

U. .... configures 1602A to transmit unformatted data from data memory at conclusion of any Trace in progress.

S. .... configures 1602A to transmit Status Byte (8 bits)

L. .... configures 1602A to transmit "Learn" message that defines its measurement configuration

V. .... Verify; causes 1602A to execute selftest and power on initialize (except HP-IB status); configure 1602A to transmit selftest result (0 = passed, 16_{10} = failed)

Other

I .... Initialize; causes 1602A to go to power on configuration (except HP-IB status)

Note. All device dependent commands are single ASCII upper case alpha characters. Characters not within command or data sets are ignored.

4.3 THE LOGIC ANALYZER UNDER BUS CONTROL

With modern microcomputer based equipment, the number of tests that should be made on a circuit in production becomes astronomical. Further, these tests often are performed by persons without an intimate knowledge of the product. Therefore, ambiguities in test results and tech-

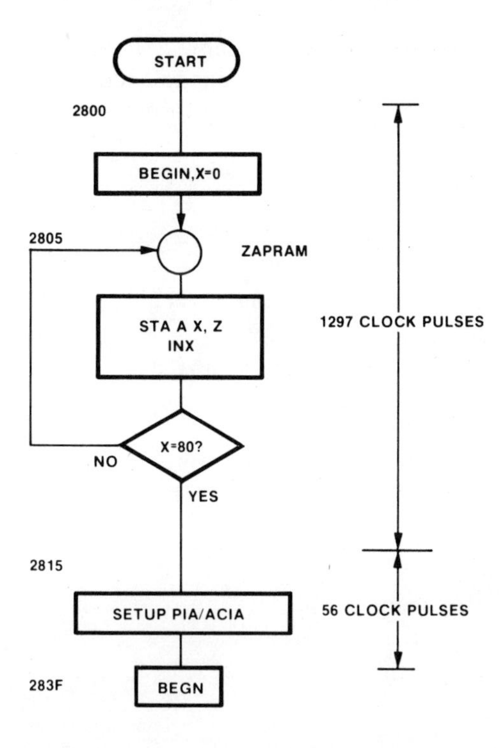

Fig. 4-8. Microprocessor start-up routine.

niques must be eliminated. Some form of automatic testing is necessary to improve throughput, improve quality, and reduce the costs of production tests. One suitable instrument combination for automatic testing is the logic state analyzer (for probing the system to be tested) and a computing controller. The two instruments would be connected via a standard interface bus such as the IEEE-488 bus discussed in Section 4.1. The operation of such a combination is best described by means of an example.

A list of the device-dependent bus commands for a typical analyzer is given in Table 4-2. To perform a test, the analyzer is programmed in the desired format for the interface bus. As an example, consider testing a system that has the start-up routine illustrated in Fig. 4-8. One technique for checking the start-up routine is to perform a trace on the microprocessor address lines. The analyzer can be formatted to trigger on the state 2800_{16}, delay by 1297^{10} clock cycles, and output the 56th sample. If this is the state $283F^{16}$, it is likely that the start-up software was executing correctly. A possible program for commanding an analyzer to do this using a Model 9825A computing controller is given in Table 4-3. Briefly, in execution the program will

(1) Dimension a register called A$ within the controller.
(2) Place all devices on the bus under bus control.
(3) Format the analyzer to the following format:

Word width 16	W16
Hexadecimal	B1
Positive Logic	P1
Negative Clock	C2
Trigger Starts Trace	M1
Decimal Delay	D1297
Trigger Word	T2800

and command the analyzer to execute ("R").
(4) Wait 2.5 seconds and then format the analyzer to output the 56th word in memory.
(5) Read the word defined in (4) into a register A$ in memory.
(6) Compare the word with the value 283F and, if they are not identical, display the message "ERROR."

Table 4-3. 9825A program summary.

COMMAND	DESCRIPTION
0 dim A$[16]	Sets length of register A$
1 llo 7	Puts 1602A to remote
2 wrt 715, "W16B1P1C2M1D1297T2800R"	Format 1602A for Trace
3 wait 2500	Wait 2500 milliseconds
4 wrt 715, "N56"	Format 1602A to talk
5 red 715, A$	Read 1602A into A$
6 if A$[13,16]="283F"; jmp 2	Test result, if pass go to line 8
7 dsp "ERROR"	Test failed; ERROR displayed
8 end	In practice second test

The program then continues with successive tests. If a test does fail, the system in Fig. 4-8 can be subdivided into smaller portions and additional tests made until the problem is isolated.

Chapter Five

Logic Analyzer Examples

5.1 INTRODUCTION

The previous chapters have described logic analyzers in some detail. This chapter will describe some measurements undertaken with logic analyzers. For illustrative purposes, the 1615A (Fig. 5-1) has been chosen for parallel measurements, and the 1640A for serial measurements. The 1615A is a combination state and timing analyzer that may be formatted as a 24-bit state analyzer, an 8-bit timing analyzer, or a simultaneous 8-bit timing and a 16-bit state analyzer. The 1615A analyzer incorporates a 24-bit wide, 256-word deep memory that operates with internal or external clocks to 20 MHz. As with all modern logic analyzers, formatting and trace specifications are programmed via the menu concept. This allows setting up many measurement functions with a minimum number of controls. Data is entered by positioning a cursor (an alternating display of video and inverse video) using the four cursor positioning keys. If the cursor is positioned to a field enclosed by brackets—such as mode, clock slope, logic polarity, or base—these selections are made with the field select key. The entries for fields without brackets are made via other keys in the entry block.

5.2 STATE ANALYZER MEASUREMENTS

Measurement 1: A Microprocessor Turn-on

When a microprocessor system is turned on, the reset circuitry directs it to a specified location in memory. In some processors, this is the program start location. In others, the processor pulls the actual start address from this initial address. The Motorola 6800 is an example of a microprocessor that uses the second technique. Upon reset, the M6800 places the value $FFFE_{16}$ on its address bus and transfers from that location the 8-bit contents to the most significant half of the 16-bit program counter. From the next location ($FFFF_{16}$) the processor collects the lower half of the 16-bit program

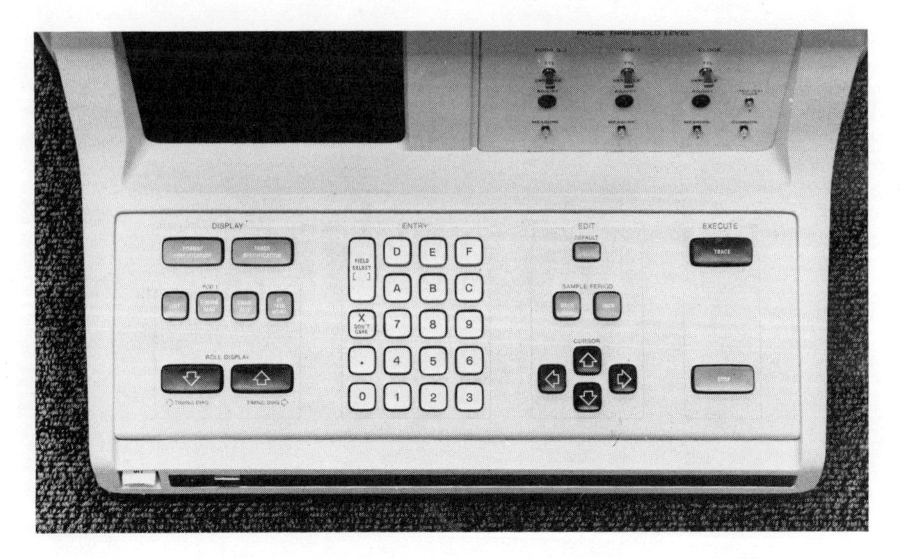

Fig. 5-1. Model 1615A logic analyzer.

counter. The addresses $FFFE_{16}$ and $FFFF_{16}$ are called the restart vector locations and the contents are the restart vector. The M6800 then jumps to the locations defined by the restart vector and commences operation from there. The cold start or reset operation of the M6800 may be observed with a logic state analyzer as illustrated in Fig. 5-2. Information is strobed into the 1615A with the same clock used by the microprocessor, the negative edge of the $\emptyset_2$clock. Address and data will only be valid when the valid memory address (VMA) line is true. Therefore, the clock is qualified with a logic 1 on VMA.

The 1615A format is placed on screen by means of a front panel control. All those displays in inverse video are alternatives available to the operator. Since state flow is to be observed, the 24-bit mode is selected. The 16 channels from pod probes 2 and 3 are connected to the address bus; these channels are given the label A. The remaining eight channels go to the data bus and are given a different label, chosen from the two remaining alternatives. Both blocks of data are programmed to be displayed in positive logic in hex base. The fourth probe contains the clock, qualifiers, and ground line. The 1615A is formatted for a negative clock. After setting up the format, the next step is to specify the trace requirements. The alternatives are placed on screen with the front panel control. The trigger word is specified as $FFFE_{16}$, the digital delay as zero, and the trigger mode as start trace.

The address lines define a unique trigger point; hence, there's no need to specify the data, and the data trace word is left as don't care. The clock is qualified by a logic 1 on the VMA line. If the M6800 system contains the $\emptyset_2$ clock ANDed with VMA, this signal can be used as the analyzer clock,

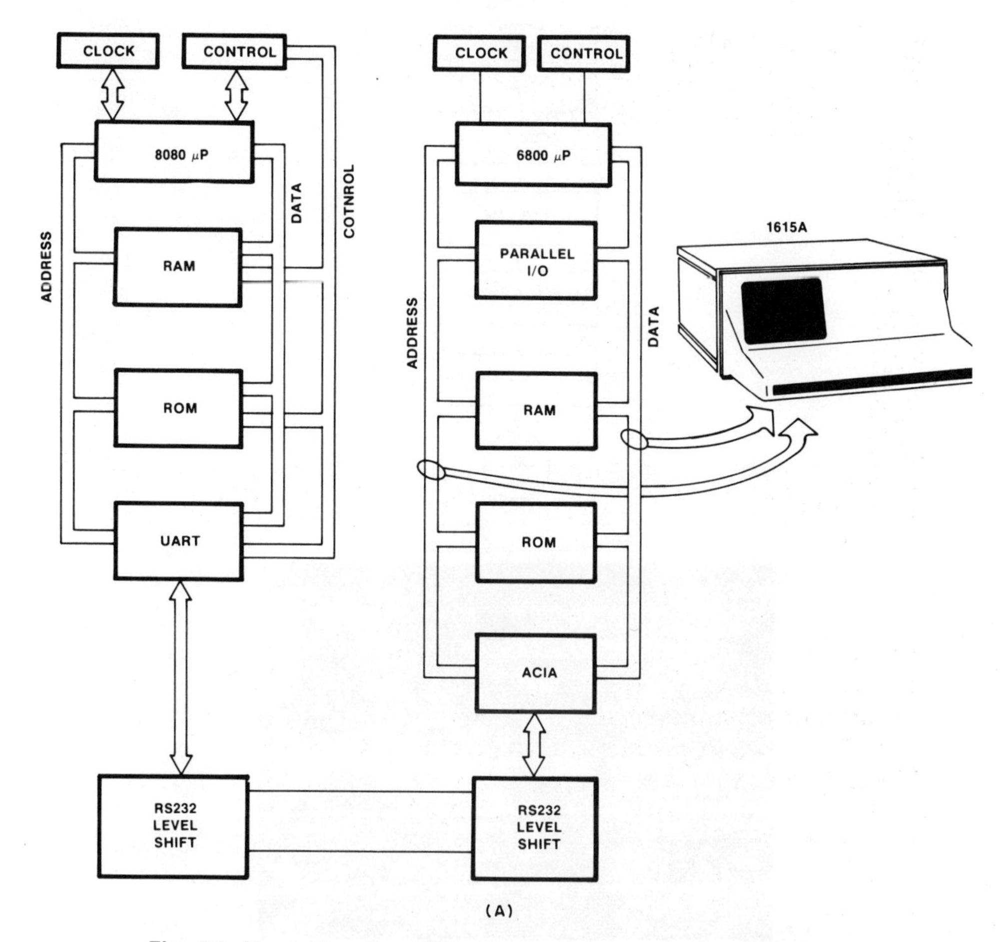

Fig. 5-2. Monitoring the 6800 microprocessor with the 1615A logic analyzer. (a) Connection diagram for measurements on the 6800 microprocessor.

making qualification unnecessary. *Note:* the 1615A has two sets of qualifiers; the off showing on-screen indicates that the second set of qualifiers is off (Fig. 5-2d).

Pressing the trace key and starting the M6800 system produces the trace of Fig. 5-2e. This trace agrees with the expected microprocessor execution of the restart program. In the first two cycles the reset vector 2800_{16} is collected, and in the third cycle the program commences operation at this location. The first operation must be an op code fetch. In this example, the code fetched is $4F_{16}$, a clear accumulator A code. The microprocessor actually executes this instruction in the next clock cycle, while the address lines are incremented in anticipation of the next instruction. The address and

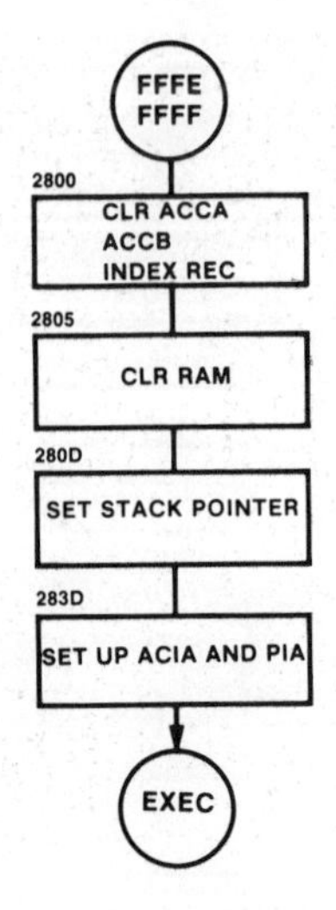

(b)

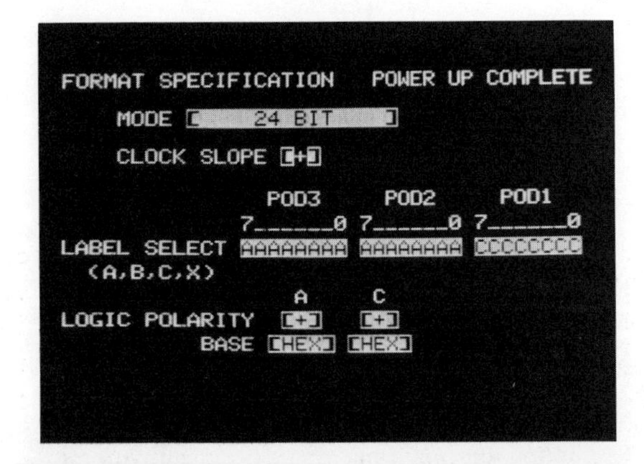

(c)

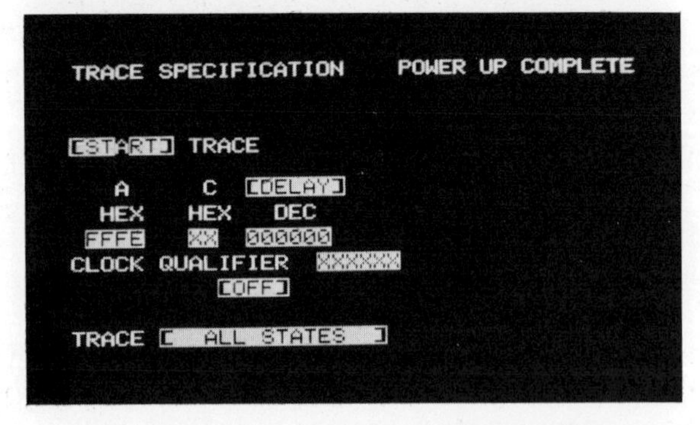

(d)

Fig. 5-2 *(cont.)* (b) Flow diagram of 6800 cold start. (c) 1615A format specification for 24-channel analysis. (d) 1615A trace specification for tracing 6800 cold start.

(e)

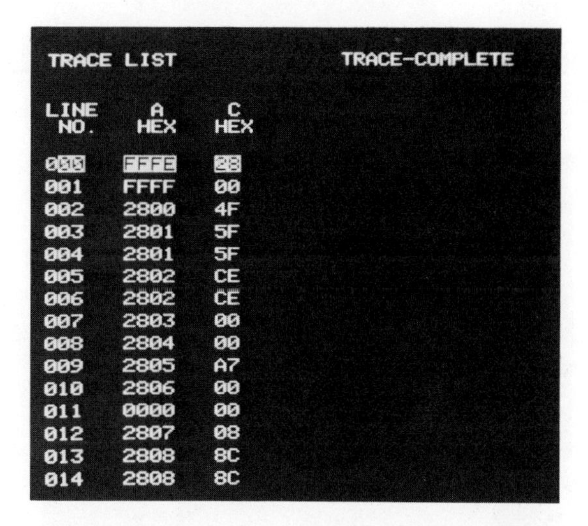

TRACE LIST TRACE-COMPLETE

LINE NO.	A HEX	C HEX
000	FFFE	28
001	FFFF	00
002	2800	4F
003	2801	5F
004	2801	5F
005	2802	CE
006	2802	CE
007	2803	00
008	2804	00
009	2805	A7
010	2806	00
011	0000	00
012	2807	08
013	2808	8C
014	2808	8C

Fig. 5-2 *(cont.)* (e) 6800 cold start program trace.

data remain fixed on the following clock cycle while the microprocessor reads the data.

Measurement 2: Trace Triggers

The system diagrammed in Fig. 5-2a reads serial data from the 8080 microprocessor and loads this data into a queue table (Fig. 5-3a). The data transferred could be monitored with a serial analyzer on the RS-232C bus. Alternatively, the data could be monitored on the parallel data bus of the M6800 system. The ACIA (asynchronous communications interface adapter) address is 4009_{16}. Tracing on this address (Fig. 5-3b) will produce a trace of the first occurrence of activity at that location (Fig. 5-3c).

Since this trace will fill the memory of the analyzer before the address 4009_{16} occurs a second time, a change is made from a trace all states to trace trigger events mode (Fig. 5-3d). Now only data or activity at the input port (address 4009_{16}) is presented on screen (Fig. 5-3e). The trace will be shown as aborted since there were only five trigger occurrences before the stop button was pressed.

Measurement 3: Occurrence Trigger

In the previous example, as each data word arrives, a subroutine is called to read and store it in a table (RAM locations 0003_{16} and 0007_{16}). As formatted in Measurement 1, the analyzer triggers on the first occurrence of the trigger word, and only the first occurrence of the subroutine will be traced, illustrating the transfer of data from location 4009_{16} (SYN-16) to the

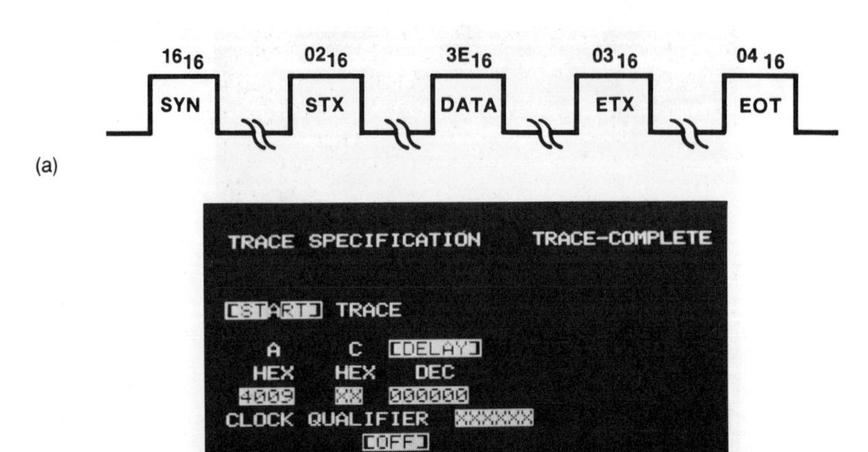

(b)

TRACE LIST TRACE-COMPLETE

LINE NO.	A HEX	C HEX
000	4009	16
001	290D	E7
002	290E	00
003	0003	16
004	290F	08
005	2910	8C
006	2910	8C
007	2911	00
008	2912	08
009	2913	27
010	2914	03
011	2915	DF
012	2916	0D
013	000D	00
014	000E	04

(c)

TRACE SPECIFICATION TRACE-COMPLETE

[START] TRACE

A	C	DELAY
HEX	HEX	DEC
4009	XX	000000

CLOCK QUALIFIER XXXXXX
[OFF]

TRACE [TRIGGER EVENTS]

(d)

(e) 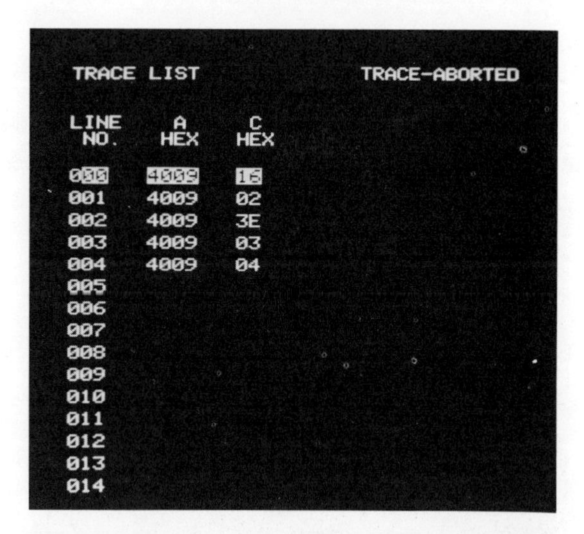

Fig. 5-3. Trace triggers to read only data at location 4009_{16}. (a) Five-part serial transmission. (b) Trace specifications for tracing program at 4009_{16}. (c) Trace of program at 4009_{16}. (d) Trace specification for tracing only activity at address 4009_{16}. (e) Trace showing five-part message read at input port address 4009_{16}.

first table location (0003_{16}). To verify that the data word, the third transmission, is read and stored in memory correctly, the delay in the trace specification may be changed to the third occurrence of the trigger word (Fig. 5-4). The first two occurrences of the trigger word are ignored, and the trace commences on the third.

If more data is required than is supplied using the trigger word alone, (as in Measurement 2), an analyzer with trigger enable and disable may be utilized. The program for the transfer of data from the data port to the queue table is shown in Fig. 5-5a. If a problem occurs, it may be necessary to monitor the seven cycles of the fetch and store operations for each of the five data transfers. This is done by enabling the logic analyzer on the address $290A_{16}$, enabling on the instruction to fetch the word from the ACIA port, and disabling on $000X_{16}$ (the queue table address). A trace triggers set to all don't cares will trace all states between $290A_{16}$ and $000X_{16}$. Once the system has stored data in the queue table (address $000X_{16}$), the trace is disabled until the address $290A_{16}$ occurs on the next pass.

The two examples in this section illustrate some of the real strengths of the logic analyzer, e.g., real time, transparent analysis of elusive program activity. Using conventional software debugging techniques, a software break would be inserted into the program just before the suspected problem point, and the program restarted the required number of times to bring it to

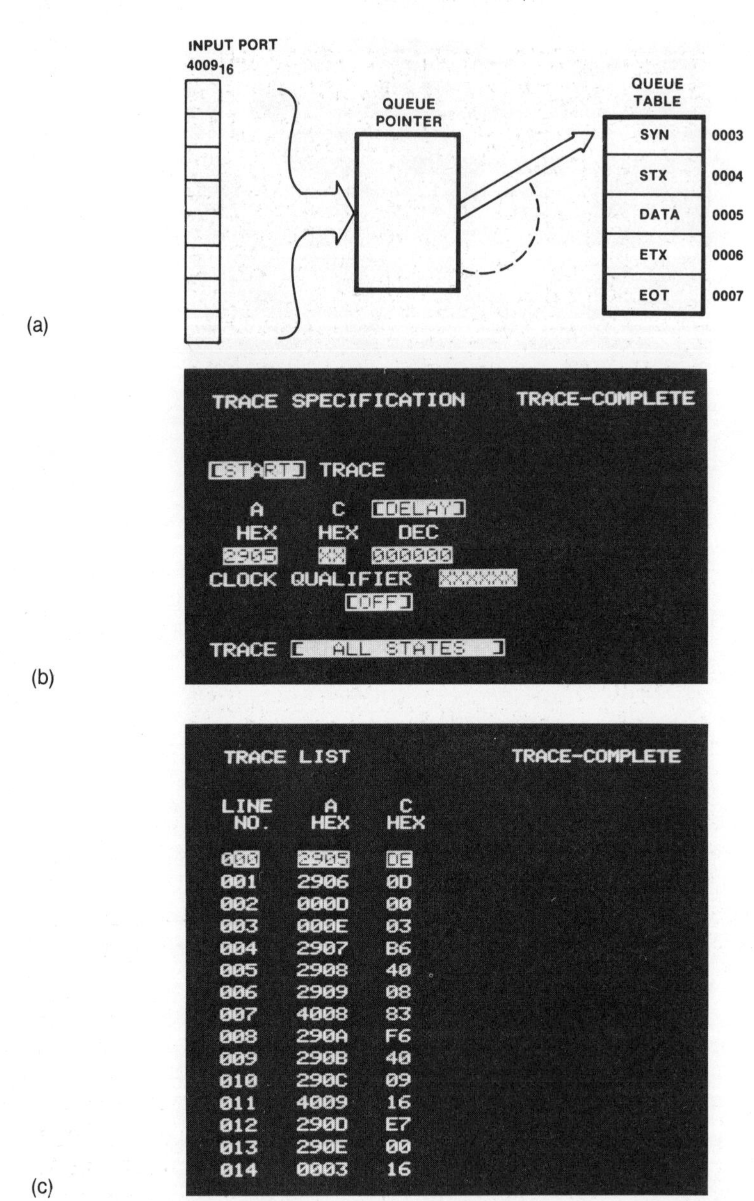

Fig. 5-4. Using Occurrence Count to trace third occurrence of subroutine. (a) Data is read at the input port and stored in a queue table in RAM. (b) Trace specifications for tracing routine at 2905_{16}. (c) Trace of program routine at 2905_{16} showing first word is read and stored in location 0003_{16}.

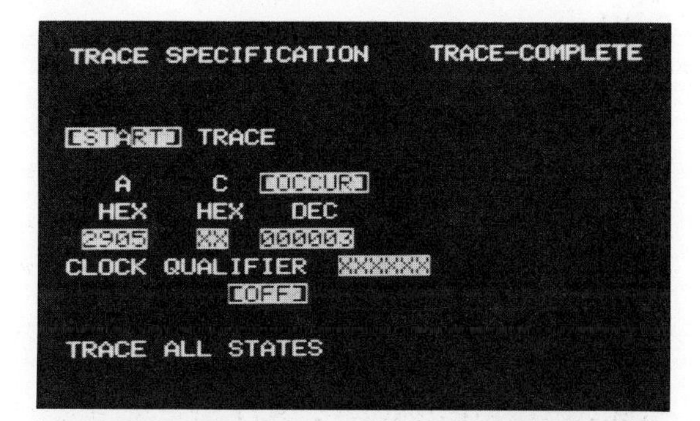

(d)

TRACE LIST TRACE-COMPLETE

LINE NO.	A HEX	C HEX
000	2905	0E
001	2906	0D
002	000D	00
003	000E	05
004	2907	B6
005	2908	40
006	2909	08
007	4008	83
008	290A	F6
009	290B	40
010	290C	09
011	4009	3E
012	290D	E7
013	290E	00
014	0005	3E

(e)

Fig. 5-4 *(cont.)* (d) Trace specifications for tracing the third occurrence of address 2905_{16}. (e) Trace of third occurrence of routine at 2905_{16} showing data word $3E_{16}$ is read and stored in location 0005_{16}.

the pass in question. In the first example quoted, the third pass gives the data word. However in more extensive systems this could be a very large number. Once the appropriate break is reached, the operator would single step the program. *Note:* this is not in real time, so problems occurring only at full speed will not be manifest in the start-stop single step routine. Further, if the system is electromechanical, the mechanical parts designed for continuous operation could respond differently, or even violently, when attempting to start and stop for software debug.

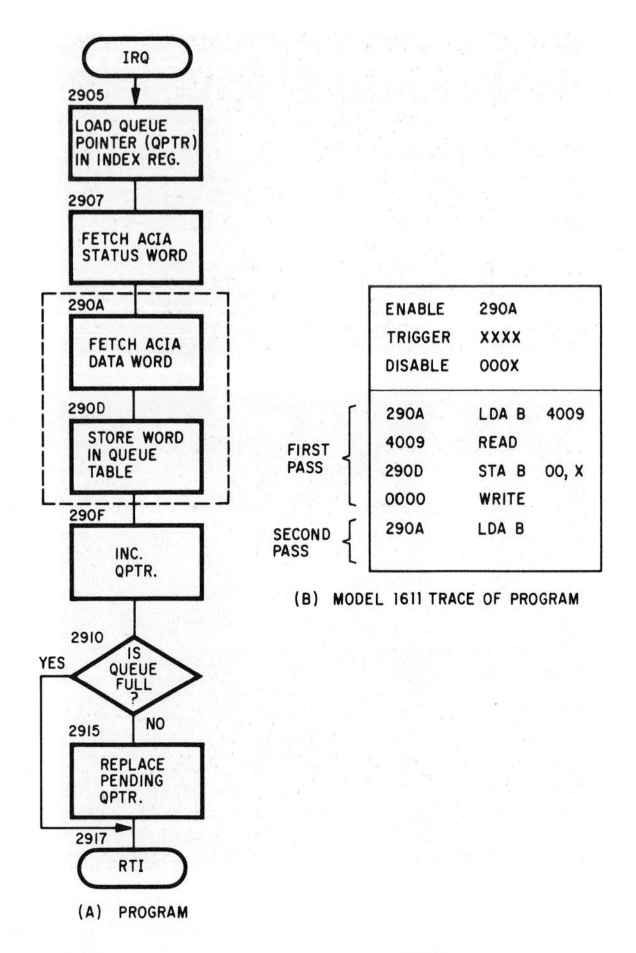

Fig. 5-5. Using trigger enable and disable to only trace a small portion of a subroutine. (a) Program. (b) Model 1611 trace of program.

Measurement 4: Interrupt Monitoring

Most data processing systems have the ability to suspend execution of the current program and perform auxiliary tasks, and then, upon completion of these tasks, return to the execution of the main program flow with all parameters maintained (internal registers, memory). This process is called an interrupt. Before the MPU reads the memory locations containing the interrupt vector and begins executing the interrupt service routine, the contents of some of the internal registers (especially the program counter) must be saved. The interrupt occurs asynchronously to the program operation. The only unique address known is the interrupt vector location $FFF8_{16}$ (and $FFF9_{16}$), and this address may be used as a trace point. (Fig. 5-6). It is

(a)

TRACE LIST TRACE-COMPLETE

LINE NO.	A HEX	C HEX
122	2A0F	7E
123	007F	0F
124	007E	2A
125	007D	03
126	007C	00
127	007B	2D
128	007A	1F
129	0079	C1
130	FFFA	29
131	FFFB	42
132	2942	0E
133	2943	7F
134	2943	7F
135	2944	40
136	2945	04

(b)

Fig. 5-6. Tracing a 6800 interrupt. (a) Trace specification for tracing a 6800 interrupt. (b) Trace of 6800 interrupt.

desirable to display program flow both before the interrupt, to show the data stored onto the stack, and after the interrupt, to show the start up of the interrupt service routine. The trigger word should therefore be programmed to occur in the center of the trace. This is achieved by end trace mode and a delay of 125. Note that the end trace mode places the trigger at word 255. Adding a delay of 125 places the trigger at word 130.

Measurement 5: Catastrophic Failure

The previous examples have all been of measurements made on operating systems. Any incorrect operations may be detected by observing the program flow and directing the trace into problem areas by selection of the trigger conditions. Should a system suffer a catastrophic failure, it is necessary to know what the processor was doing when the failure occurred. Such failures may be the result of an intermittent component, a faulty connec-

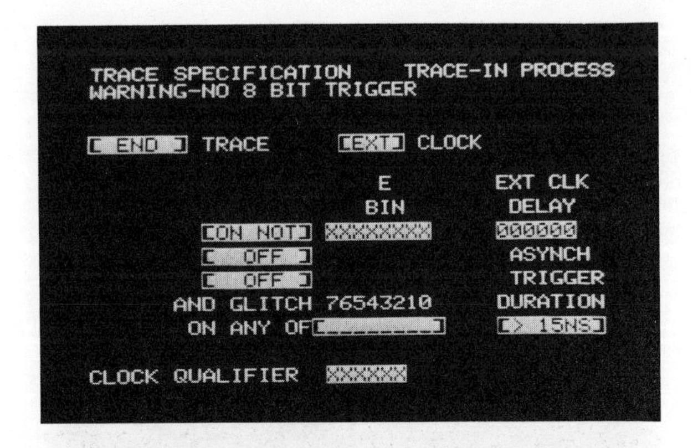

(a)

TRACE LIST TRACE-ABORTED

LINE NO.	E BIN
241	10110111
242	01000000
243	00000100
244	01010000
245	10000100
246	10110000
247	10110111
248	01000000
249	00000100
250	00010000
251	00111001
252	10010110
253	00101001
254	10100110
255	00110010

(b)

Fig. 5-7. Tracing a catastrophic failure. (a) Trace specifications that guarantee that no trigger will be found. (b) Record of events leading to clock or qualifier failure.

tion, or a software problem (in which case the control signals would disappear when a certain subroutine is executed).

By tracing in the end trace mode, the logic analyzer acquires data until a trace point is located. By purposely selecting a trace point that never occurs, the logic analyzer continues to monitor the buses until the clock or qualified clock ceases. On the clock failure, the analyzer will have frozen in memory the events leading to the clock failure.

In the 8-bit configuration, the 1615A has a NOT Triggering facility. If not don't care is specified as the trigger, a condition that can never be satisfied, data ripples through the 1615A until the clock fails. At that point, the events leading to the failure are trapped for subsequent investigation (Fig. 5-7).

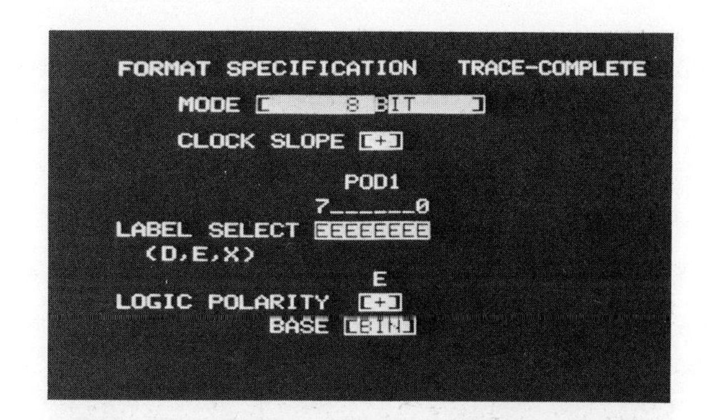

(a)

TRACE SPECIFICATION TRACE-COMPLETE

[END] TRACE [INT] CLOCK 100NS/CLK

E [EXT CLK]
BIN DELAY
[ON] 11111111 000000
[OFF] ASYNCH
[OFF] TRIGGER
AND GLITCH 76543210 DURATION
ON ANY OF[________] [> 15NS]

DELAY QUALIFIER XXXXXX

(b)

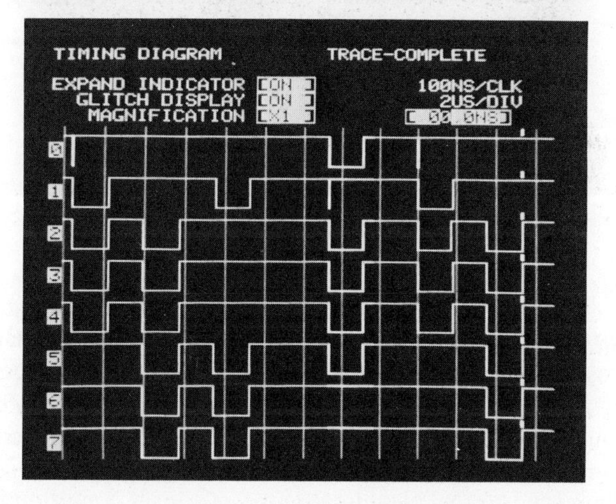

(c)

Fig. 5-8. Timing waveforms for 8080 data bus. (a) Format specifications for tracing eight lines asynchronously. (b) Trace specifications for tracing on all lines high. (c) Asynchronous trace of eight lines.

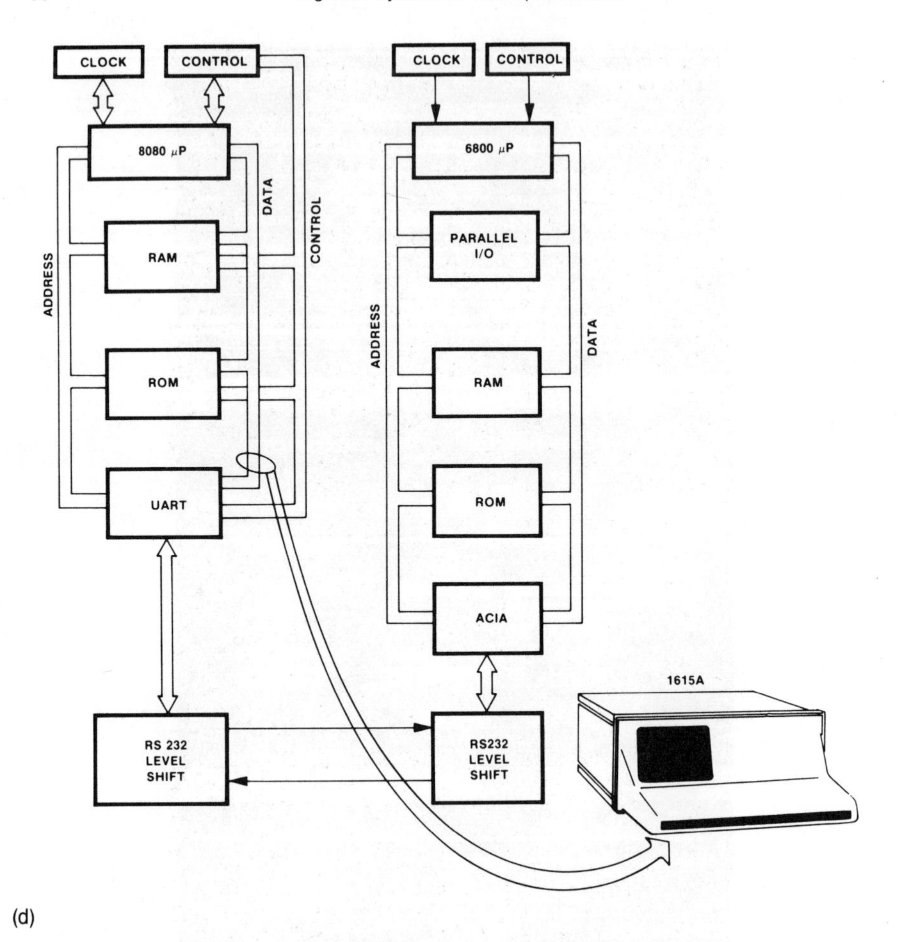

(d)

Fig. 5-8 *(cont.)* (d) Hookup for measurements on data bus.

5.3 TIMING ANALYZER MEASUREMENTS

Measurement 1: Timing Relationships on Data Bus

In most digital systems, the timing relationship among control lines may be critical. If the data of interest occurs infrequently and/or involves several channels, an asynchronous timing analyzer can be applied effectively. This is illustrated in Fig. 5-8d where the 8-bit timing pod of the 1615A has been connected to the 8080 data bus. The trigger condition is set to all highs and the internal clock, to 100 ns (10 MHz) (Figs. 5-8a and 5-8b). The resulting timing diagram is shown in Fig. 5-8c.

The time interval between the glitch on channel 1 and the negative-going transition could be measured automatically using the microprocessor-based logic analyzer. The edge of the intensified portion of the trace is first

(a)

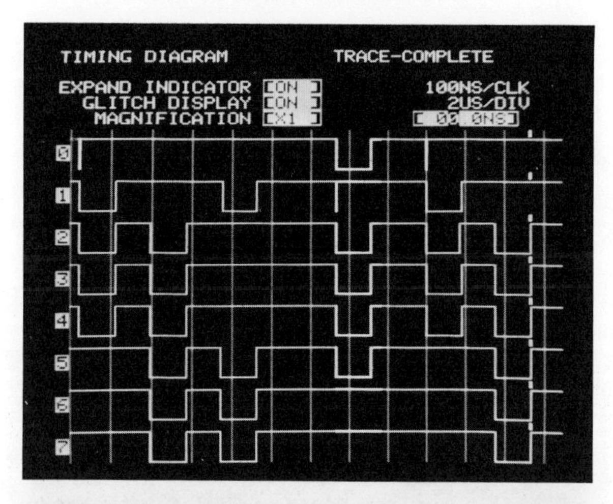

(b)

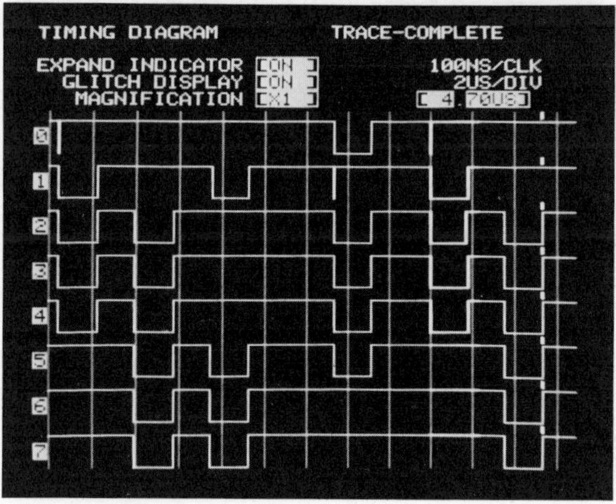

Fig. 5-9. Time interval measurement with a logic analyzer. (a) Asynchronous trace with reference point set to zero. (b) Time interval from reference point is read directly.

positioned at the glitch by using the display roll controls, and the time is initialized to zero by means of the field select control. Rolling the intensified display will permit the time intervals to be read directly; the time shown now corresponds to the amount of displacement of the intensified marker from the point at which it was set to zero (Fig. 5-9).

Measurement 2: Triggering on Transient States

The search for a trigger point in asynchronous analysis must be done independently of the sample rate and sample points. A trace point is recognized whenever the state of the lines matches the trigger conditions. The re-

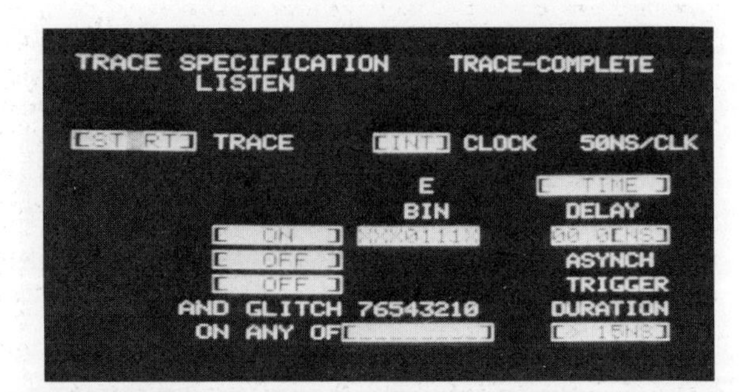

(a)

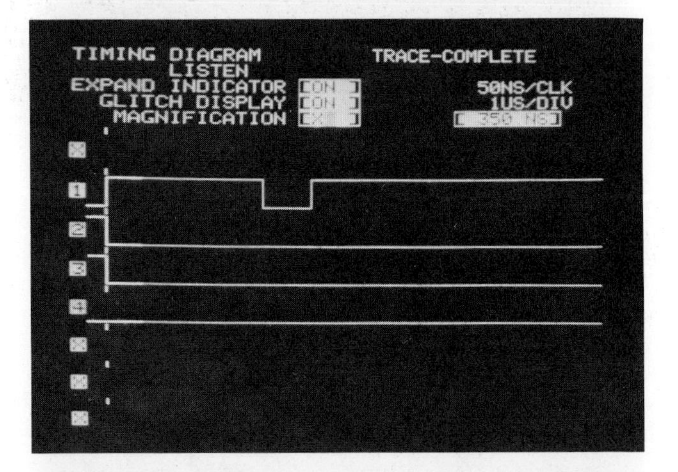

(b)

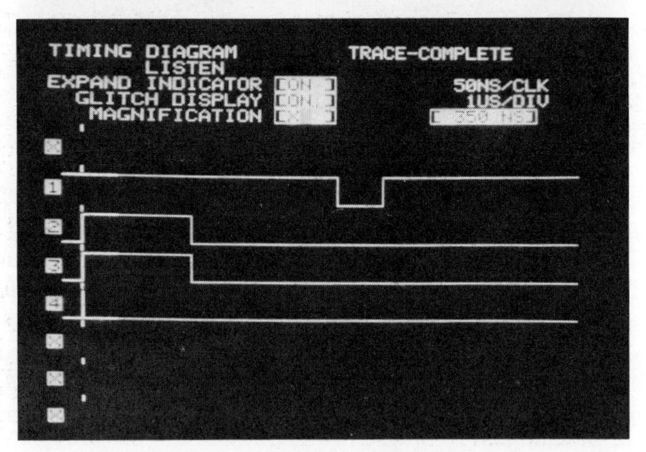

(c)

Fig. 5-10. Effect of trigger word filter width on display. (a) The trigger width has been set to 15 ns. The analyzer will now trigger on any transient states that satisfy the Boolean or state conditions. See (b), (c), and (d). (e) The trigger width is now set to a value greater than 15 ns, which inhibits triggering on transients. Now, even in a continuous mode, a steady trace results. See (f). (f) Steady trace.

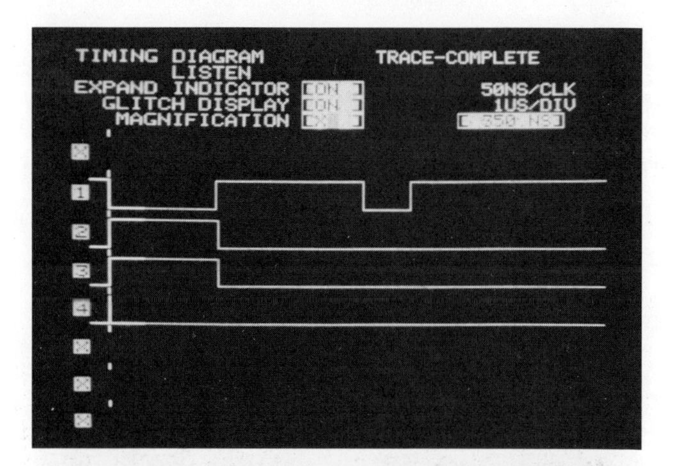
TIMING DIAGRAM
LISTEN
TRACE-COMPLETE
EXPAND INDICATOR [ON]
GLITCH DISPLAY [ON]
MAGNIFICATION [X]
50NS/CLK
1US/DIV
[350 NS]

(d)

TRACE SPECIFICATION
LISTEN
TRACE-COMPLETE
[START] TRACE
[INT] CLOCK
50NS/CLK
E
BIN
[TIME]
DELAY
[ON]
XXX0111X
00 0[NS]
[OFF]
ASYNCH
[OFF]
TRIGGER
AND GLITCH 76543210
DURATION
ON ANY OF[________]
[200NS]

(e)

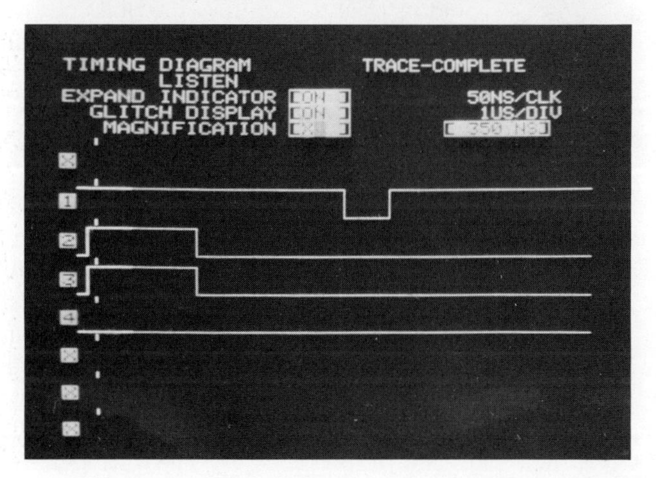
TIMING DIAGRAM
LISTEN
TRACE-COMPLETE
EXPAND INDICATOR [ON]
GLITCH DISPLAY [ON]
MAGNIFICATION [X]
50NS/CLK
1US/DIV
[350 NS]

(f)

sult may be a valid trace point or a transitional state. This is illustrated in Fig. 5-10 where a trigger duration of only 15 ns results in several traces that have triggered on transitional states. Should it become necessary to trigger only on valid states, this may be done as shown in Fig. 5-10f where the trigger duration has been made larger than any transient. Here a steady trace is obtained even in the continuous trace mode.

The reader may obtain a better understanding of the explanation of various displays of Fig. 5-10 by referring to Section 3.4.

Measurement 3: Tracing on Glitches

Any narrow spikes on control lines may cause erroneous clocking of data. Alternatively, these glitches may enter the interrupt lines, causing the processor to enter an unexpected interrupt routine. The first place to observe activity is on the interrupt line and its associated circuitry. In this example, the interrupt line is driven by a monostable. The 1615A probes are connected to the monostable output and input, and the analyzer set to trigger on an interrupt. Interrupts are found to occur when the normal input of the monostable is pulsed (Fig. 5-11b) and sometimes when it is not (Fig. 5-11c). For further investigation of these interrupts, channel 5 is connected to the other monostable input, which is normally pulled high. The glitch that is probably causing the interrupt is found.

To select only the bad interrupt for further investigations, the trace point is set to an interrupt on channel 7 and a glitch on channel 5. This directs future traces to only those conditions where the problem is occurring. The remaining probes could be used to monitor other lines physically close to this problem line. By observation, the source of the glitch is found.

5.4 COMBINATION STATE AND TIME MEASUREMENTS

Measurement 1: Timing Analyzer Triggers State

In the example just given, the operator may wish to know if the glitch was related to the program. To answer this question, two simultaneous measurements are required: an asynchronous timing measurement triggered on the occurrence of the erroneous interrupt and a synchronous state measurement triggered by the same trace point. This provides a direct relationship between the program flow and the hardware signals within the system (Fig. 5-12).

To acquire both synchronous and asynchronous data simultaneously, the 1615A is formatted as shown in Fig. 5-13a. The trace point selected in example 5.3.3 (low on channel 7 and a glitch on channel 5) remains unchanged. This trigger point now triggers the state or synchronous portion as well as the timing. As shown in Fig. 5-13b, it is specified that the trace point halts or ends the capture of synchronous data. The resultant trace gives two separate displays with a common trace point. As before, the 8-bit asyn-

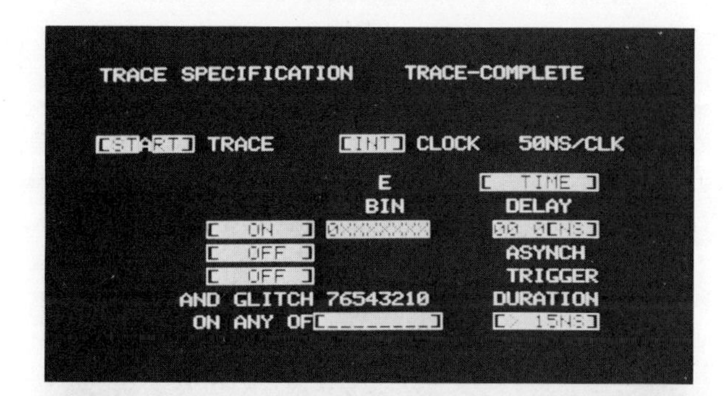

(a)

(b)

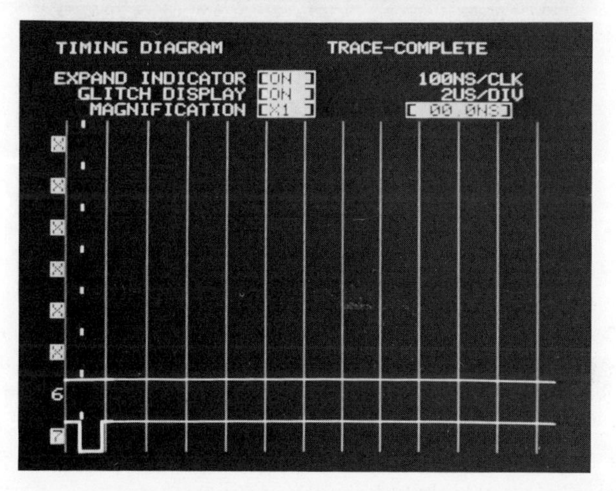

(c)

Fig. 5-11. Tracing a faulty interrupt with a logic analyzer. (a) Trace specifications for tracing when interrupt line goes low. (b) Trace showing interrupt line low when "one shot" is pulsed. (c) Trace showing "false interrupt"—one which occurs without the "one shot" receiving a pulse.

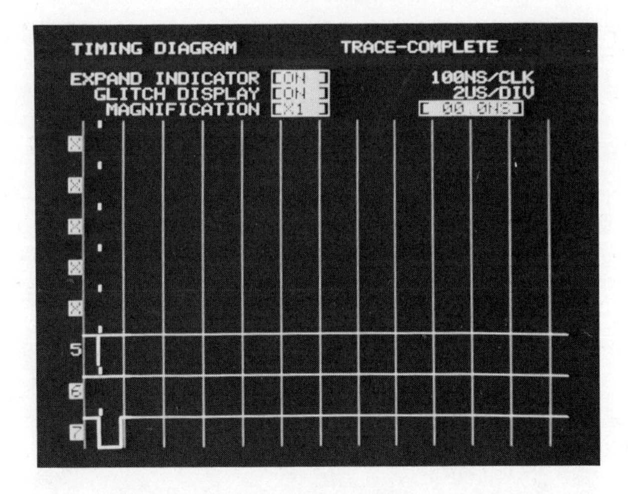

(d)

CS U18 pin 11
I/O WRITE
I/O READ U25 pin 1
U4
8080
INT SYNC
NORMAL INPUT

(e)

TRACE SPECIFICATION
LISTEN
TRACE-COMPLETE
[START] TRACE
[INT] CLOCK
50NS/CLK
E
BIN
[TIME]
DELAY
[ON]
[OFF]
[OFF]
ASYNCH
TRIGGER
AND GLITCH 76543210
DURATION
ON ANY OF

(f)

Fig. 5-11 *(cont.)* (d) Trace showing that false interrupt is apparently glitch induced. (e) Interrupt circuit. (f) Trace specifications for tracing only if interrupt line is pulsed when a glitch is present on the monostable input.

chronous display reveals the glitch induced interrupt (Fig. 5-13c). Repeated observations show that the trace point in the 16-bit synchronous display occurs at the same time as the intensified word 8080_{16}. Checking the listing reveals that the address 8080_{16} refers to the I/O port. A second trace, after connecting other lines that relate to an I/O port, shows a coincidence between the I/O read signal and the glitch. The physical layout of the I/O read line and the monostable is now investigated to eliminate coupling between the two lines.

Measurement 2: State Analyzer Triggers Timing

The interrupt problem discussed in the previous example could have also been solved from the software or program point of view. In this case, the interrupt vector address (0030_{16}) is selected as a trace point. The activity on the various control lines preceding this point is traced by selecting the 16-bit trace point to end the 8-bit asynchronous trace (Fig. 5-14). The results are identical to those of the previous measurement.

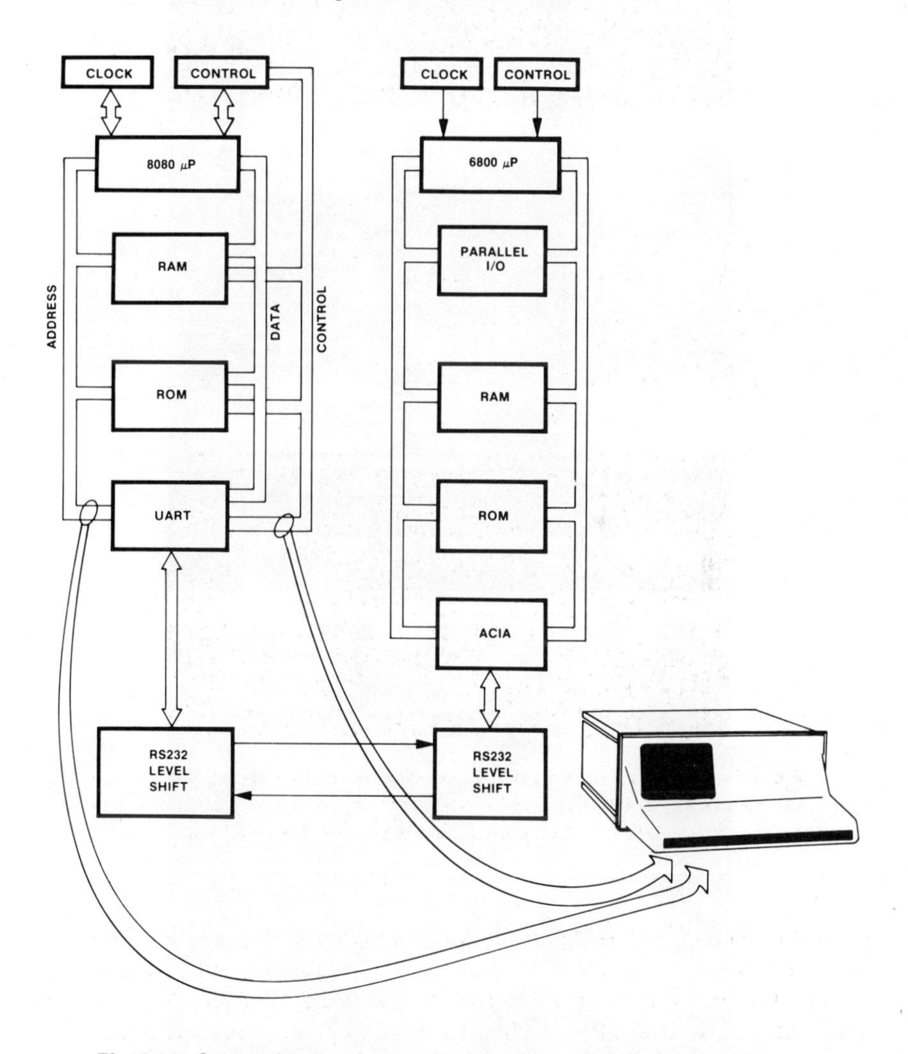

Fig. 5-12. System hookup for monitoring address bus and control lines.

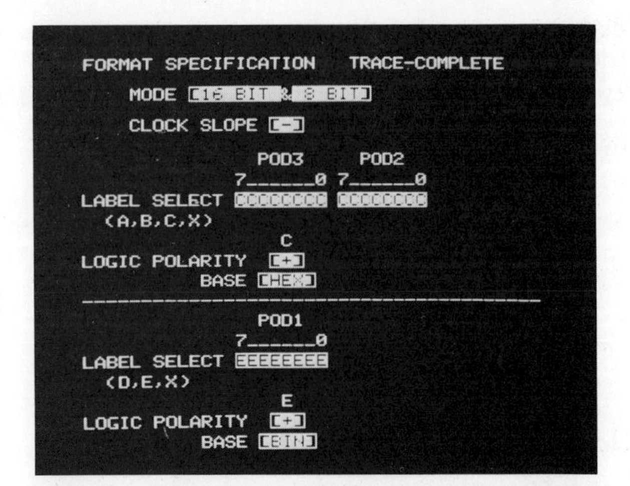
FORMAT SPECIFICATION TRACE-COMPLETE
MODE [16 BIT & 8 BIT]
CLOCK SLOPE [-]
POD3 POD2
7______0 7______0
LABEL SELECT CCCCCCCC CCCCCCCC
(A,B,C,X)
C
LOGIC POLARITY [+]
BASE [HEX]
POD1
7______0
LABEL SELECT EEEEEEEE
(D,E,X)
E
LOGIC POLARITY [+]
BASE [BIN]

(a)

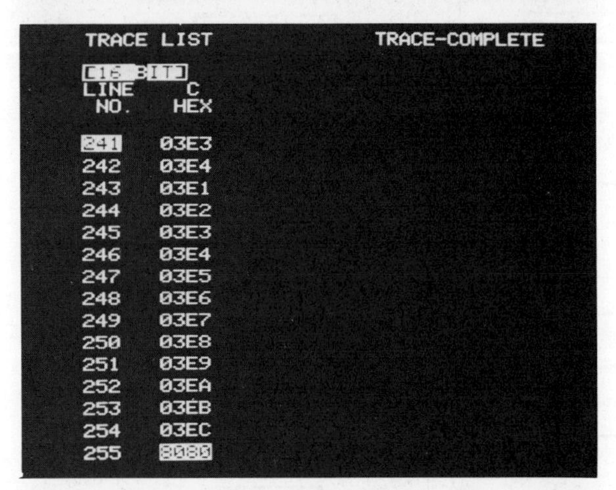
TRACE LIST TRACE-COMPLETE
[16 BIT]
LINE NO.
C HEX
241 03E3
242 03E4
243 03E1
244 03E2
245 03E3
246 03E4
247 03E5
248 03E6
249 03E7
250 03E8
251 03E9
252 03EA
253 03EB
254 03EC
255 8080

(b)

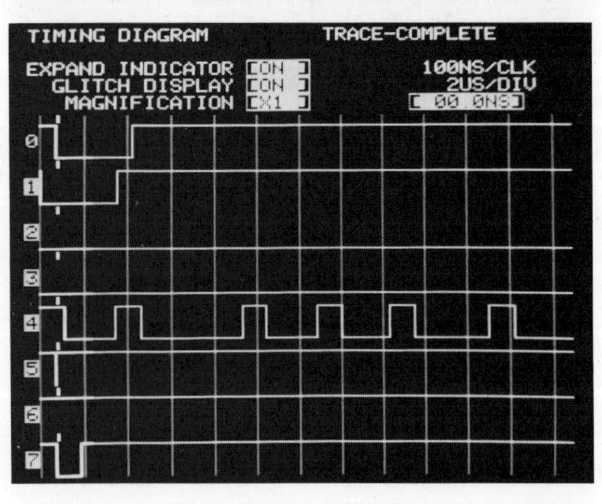
TIMING DIAGRAM TRACE-COMPLETE
EXPAND INDICATOR [ON]
GLITCH DISPLAY [ON]
MAGNIFICATION [X1]
100NS/CLK
2US/DIV
[00.0NS]
0
1
2
3
4
5
6
7

(c)

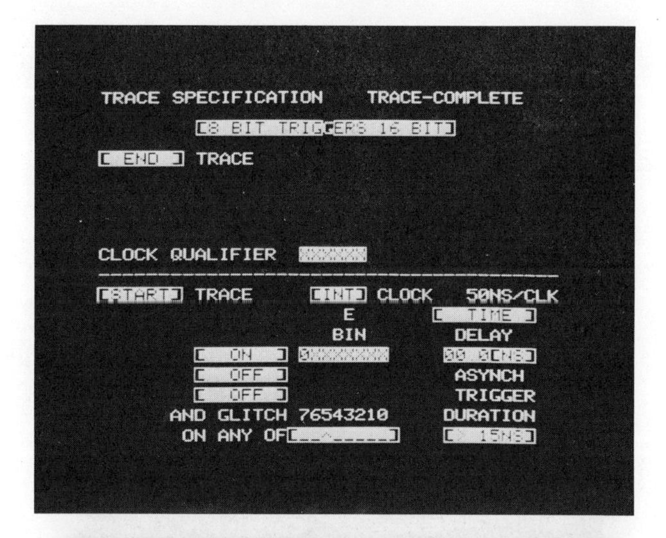

(d)

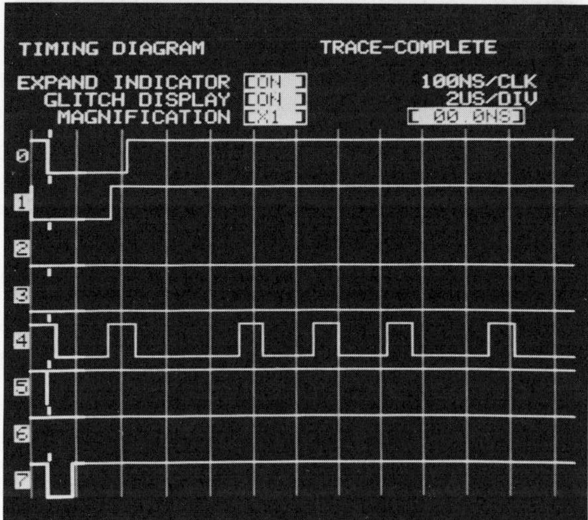

(e)

Fig. 5-13. Simultaneous state and time measurements. (a) Format specifications for simultaneous tracing of control (asynchronously) lines and the processor address bus (synchronously). Clock source is 8080 sync. (b) Trace specifications for tracing on false interrupt with simultaneous trace of address bus. (c) Trace of false interrupt. (d) Trace of address bus activity preceding the false interrupt. Note that the trigger always occurs when the system is in the state 8080_{16}. (e) Tracing additional control lines connected with "read" operations reveals a coincidence between I/O read negative edge and glitch.

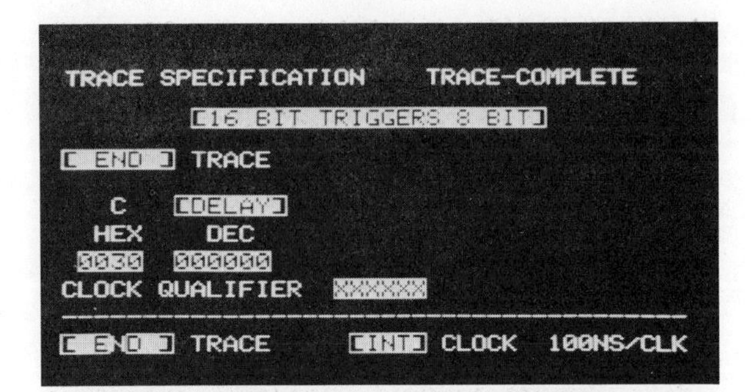

(a)

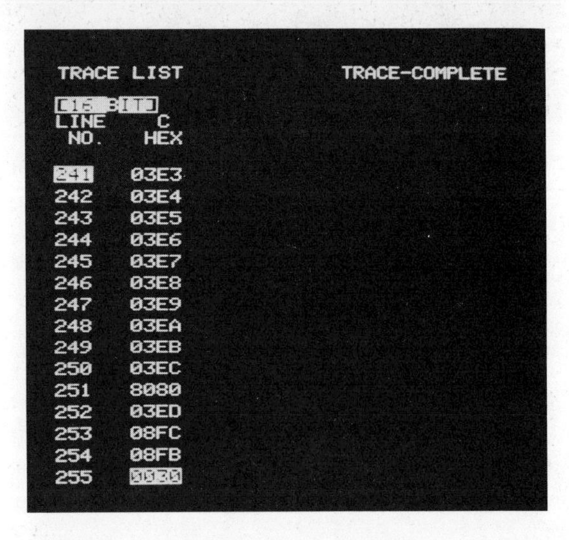

(b)

Fig. 5-14. State analyzer triggers timing measurement. (a) Trace specifications for tracing on the interrupt service routine and capturing preceding control bus activity. (b) Trace ending on occurrence of interrupt service routine. Note the IN 80 execution four states earlier (line 251). Hence, the system was executing an I/O instruction when the interrupt occurred.

5.5 SERIAL ANALYZER MEASUREMENTS

Measurement 1: Monitoring an RS-232C Bus

As an illustration of the application of serial analysis, a 1640A will be used to monitor the RS-232C link between the two halves of the system shown in Fig. 5-15. The 1640A (Fig. 5-16) utilizes the menu concept for formatting and specifying the trace. The 1640A may be configured to various RS-232C applications with the interface matrix located on top of the analyzer. Figure 5-17 shows a typical matrix configuration for the monitor mode. The pin connection shows that line 2 of the RS-232C link is defined by the 1640A as the transmitted data; line 3, the received data, and so forth. These

(c)

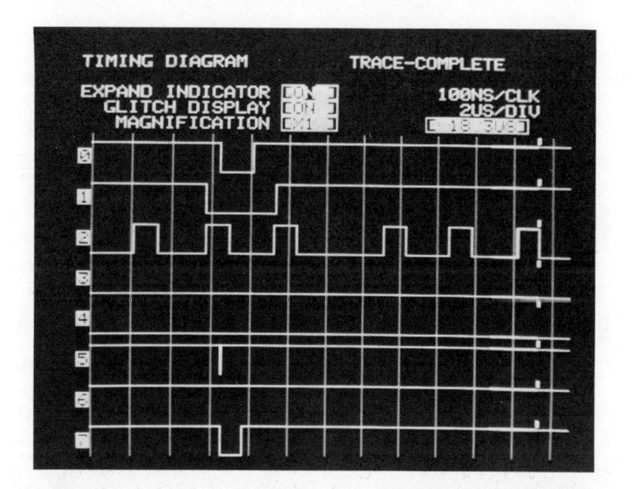

Fig. 5-14 *(cont.).* (c) Asynchronous trace of control bus activity prior to the interrupt. Cause of interrupt appears to be glitch induced from I/O read pulse, line 0.

lines could be reversed by altering the pin connections. The LEDs on the extreme left indicate activity on any of the bus lines that are monitored by the 1640A via the matrix pin connections.

Calling up the format menu, the field select key allows the operator to set the appropriate format to monitor the bus. In this example, it is 7-bit ASCII, asynchronous transmission with one stop bit plus an even parity check bit. The system operates at 300 bits/s (Fig. 5-18a).

In the monitor mode, as shown in Fig. 5-18b, no trigger word is defined. Consequently, when the run button is pushed, the data on the bus is

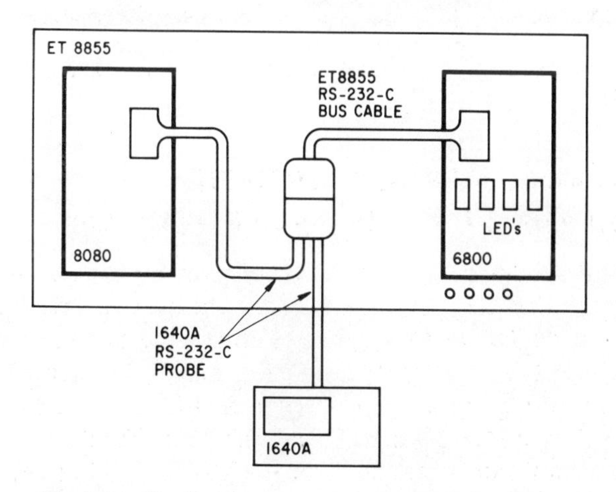

Fig. 5-15. Hookup for measurements on RS-232C bus.

Fig. 5-16. 1640A serial network analyzer.

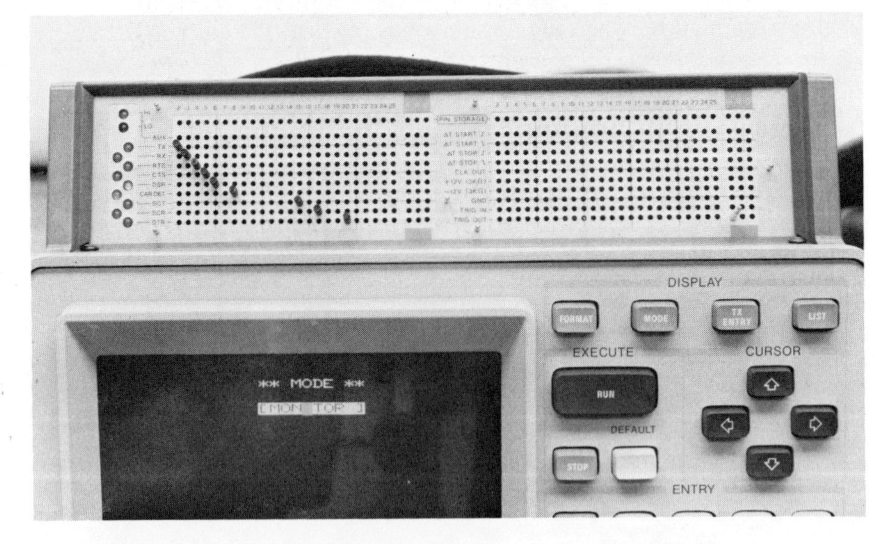

Fig. 5-17. Matrix connections for monitor mode on the 1640A.

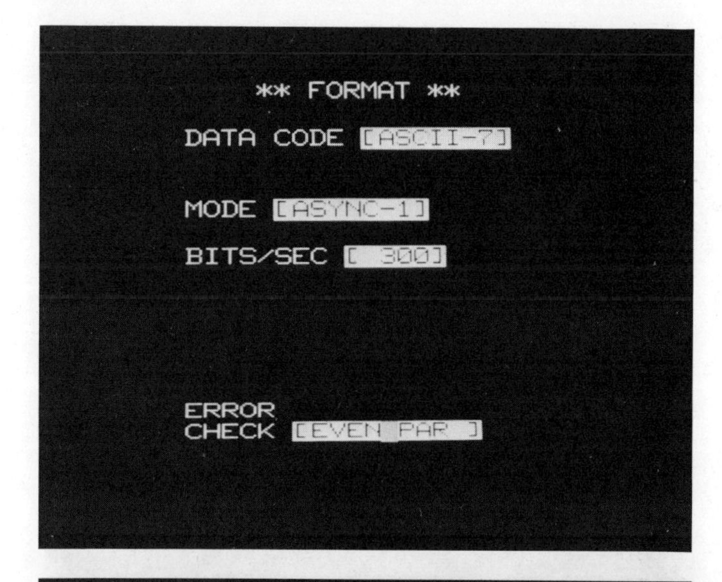

(a)

** MODE **
[MONITOR]
TRIG SOURCE [RX CHAR SEQ]
RUN MODE [COUNT TRIGGERS]
TRIG
SUPPRESS [OFF]

(b)

Fig. 5-18. Monitoring a RS-232C bus. (a) Format. (b) Mode.

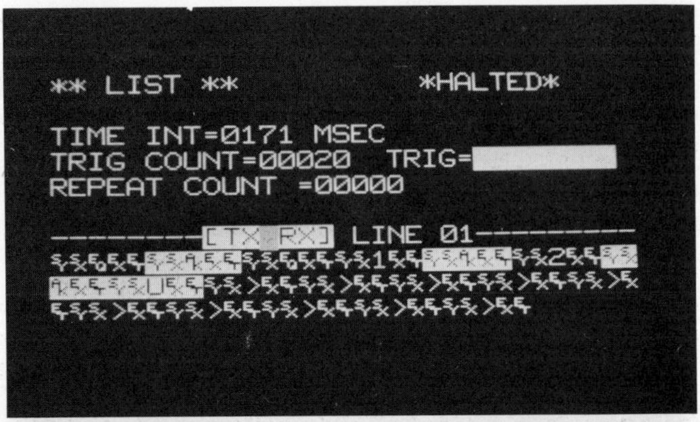

** LIST ** *HALTED*

TIME INT=0171 MSEC
TRIG COUNT=00020 TRIG=
REPEAT COUNT =00000

---------[TX RX] LINE 01----------

(c)

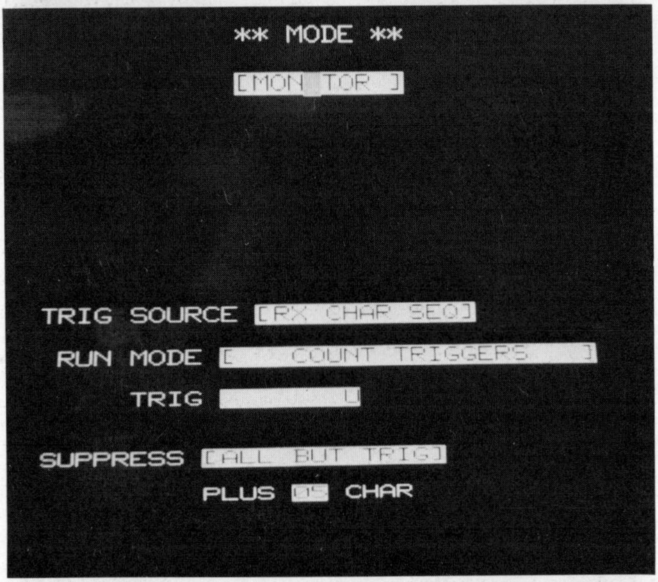

** MODE **

[MON TOR]

TRIG SOURCE [RX CHAR SEQ]

RUN MODE [COUNT TRIGGERS]

TRIG U

SUPPRESS [ALL BUT TRIG]

PLUS 05 CHAR

(d)

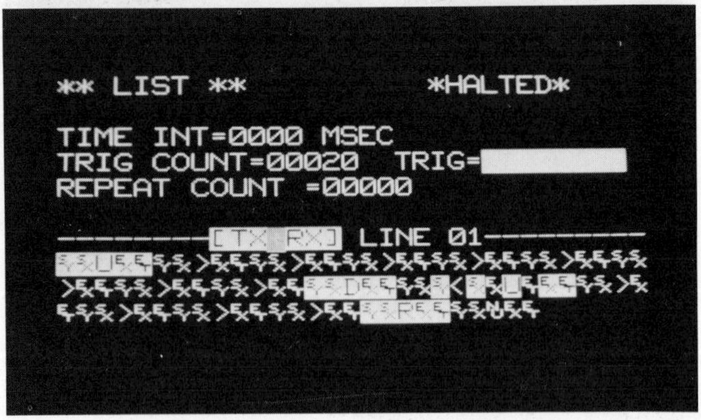

** LIST ** *HALTED*

TIME INT=0000 MSEC
TRIG COUNT=00020 TRIG=
REPEAT COUNT =00000

---------[TX RX] LINE 01----------

(e)

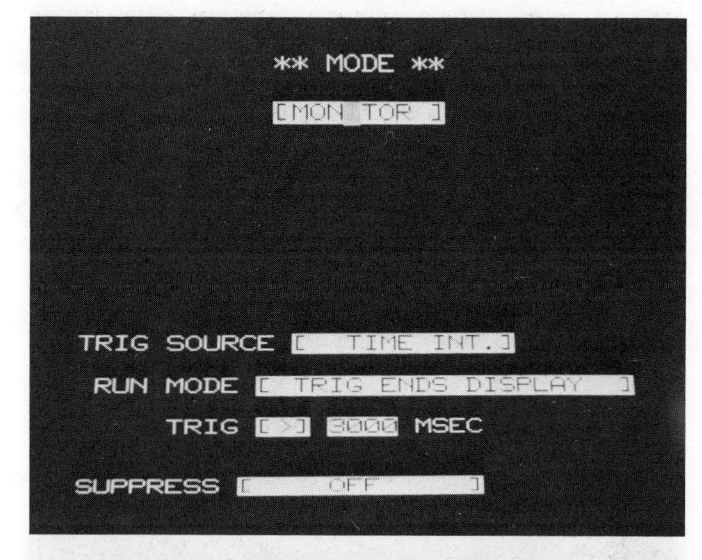

(a)

** LIST ** *HALTED*
TIME INT=3928 MSEC
TRIG COUNT=00001
REPEAT COUNT =00000
--------[TX RX] LINE 01---------

(b)

Fig. 5-19. Time interval measurements with the 1640A. (a) Matrix. (b) Mode.

Fig. 5-18. *(cont.*, opposite page). (c) Typical list. (d) Trigger on NOT U. (e) List generated using NOT U as trigger.

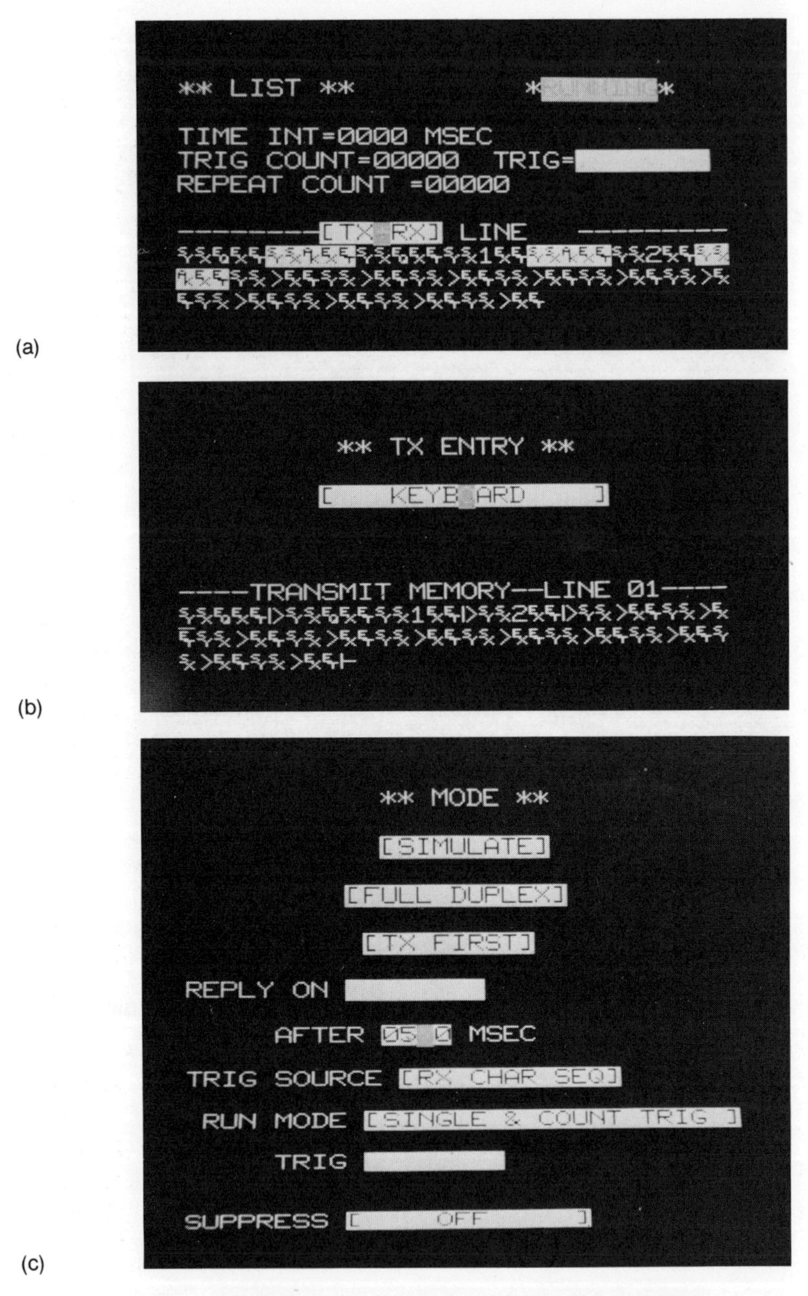

Fig. 5-20. Simulate measurements with the 1640A.

trapped immediately (Fig. 5-17c). To differentiate received and transmitted data, the 1640A displays received data in inverse video. The field select key allows either or both sets of data to be displayed on the screen. When both

(d)

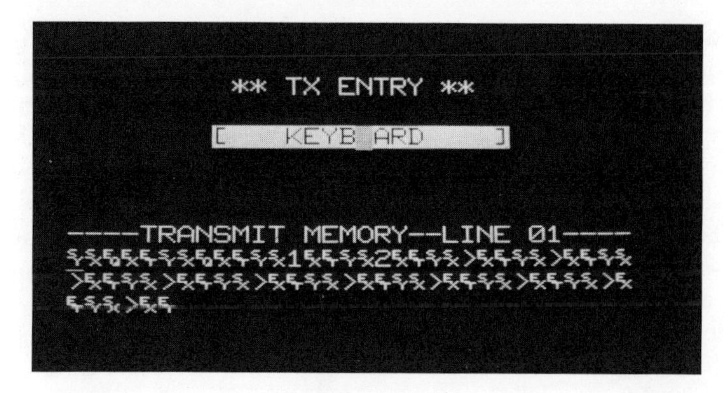

Fig. 5-20. *(cont.).*

are displayed, the transmit and receive data are interweaved in the sequence in which they occur.

In many systems, between each transmission there will be many null and/or sync characters. The 1640A suppress facility eliminates these characters. A more selective trace could be obtained. This is illustrated in Fig. 5-18d where the display is qualified to be the trigger word plus the next five characters. Since in this example the trigger is chosen to be the received character "NOT U," the full "reply" to all requests but "U" will be observed. For purposes of this illustration, "U" is assumed to be a valid transmission. Therefore, the analyzer is programmed to trigger or trap out on invalid received data.

Measurement 2: Trapping a Time-out Error

Many systems have a requirement that all transmissions be acknowledged within a specified time. If there is no response within this time, the master would time-out and enter an error recovery routine. To determine that the 6800 system in Fig. 5-15 does respond within three seconds of receiving a transmission from the 8080, the timing facility of the 1640A may be utilized. The time interval measurement would be started by a transmission (line 2) and stopped by a received signal (line 3). The 1640A is programmed to trigger on time intervals greater than 3000 ms (Fig. 5-19a). In the trigger ends trace mode, the list of Fig. 5-19b is obtained, and the trace halting 64 characters or two display lines follows the time interval violation. The display also shows the time of the interval that caused the trigger.

Measurement 3: Simulation

One important facility available with the 1640A is the simulate capability. By learning the protocol of the transmitter, or alternatively by entering it via the keyboard, the 1640A may simulate part of the system. To use the learn facility, the 1640A is first operated in its normal monitor mode and a list obtained (Fig. 5-20a). With the transmitter entry menu, all the transmitted data (i.e., video data) may be loaded into the transmit memory. The data is then edited, using the insert and delete keys, and the message broken up into the appropriate blocks by inserting continue symbols with an end symbol at the conclusion (Fig. 5-20b).

To actually perform the simulation, the 8080 system is removed and the 1640A is placed in the simulate mode (Fig. 5-20c). In this example, the 1640A is configured as full-duplex and is programmed to initiate the conversation. To actually simulate, the cursor is moved back to the simulate mode (Fig. 5-20d) and the run button is pushed. The 1640A is now simulating the 8080 system; it first sends out the sequence stored in its transmit memory, up to the first continue symbol (Fig. 5-20b). The next block of data is then transmitted 500 ms after the reply from the 6800.

APPENDIX

Logic Analyzer Terms and Definitions

Active Clock Edge The clock transition on which all receivers (listeners) interpret the data on the bus. A logic analyzer must monitor the system using this same active edge as its clock.
Address Bus That bus in the system used to address or define the memory or device location enabled.
Algorithm A detailed sequence of steps for solving problems or generating signals in digital systems.
Aliasing The display of a sampled waveform, when the sample rate is slower than the data rate.
Arm An input or condition that must occur prior to the analyzer trigger conditions being recognized. See Trigger Enable.
Assembly Language A language of mnemonics that defines the machine instruction to be executed.
Asynchronous Analyzer Data is traced asynchronous to system under test. See Timing Analyzer.
Asynchronous Data Data that is not referenced to time. The completion of one operation signals the next operation.
Asynchronous Triggering Triggering of timing analyzer by signals independent of the analyzer clock.
Bits/Byte The number of bits formatted as a byte in a logic analyzer.
Bus System A network of paths or set of lines that facilitate data flow in a digital system. The common buses are the address, data, and control buses.
Bytes/Syn Sets number of bytes displayed following a synchronizing pulse on a serial analyzer.
Central Processing Unit The heart of a computer system. No standard design exists, but most contain many or all of the following blocks: ALU, instruction decode/control, registers, and system bus interface(s).
Clock A generator of pulses that controls the timing of all operations in a digital system. In many systems there will be more than one clock. Both the system and any monitoring instrument must interpret the data on an active clock edge when all data are valid.

Clock Qualifier(s) External analyzer inputs that define additional conditions as to when data may be sampled. A sample is taken only on an active clock edge provided the clock qualifier conditions are satisfied.
Clock Slope The transition or active edge at which the analyzer samples data.
Combinational Trigger The pattern of 0's, 1's, and don't cares set on all channels that, when matched by the sampled data, causes a trace to commence.
Compare Comparison of new data with old stored data, often displayed in exclusive-OR format. See also Halt.
Control Bus The bus that passes signals that police or control the system operation.
Count Measurements Logic analyzer facility to count the number of occurrences of a specified state as it occurs.
Data Bus Those lines or channels that are used to pass bidirectional data between enabled devices in a digital system.
Data Domain A domain concerned with the total amount of data that must be collected at every event-time in order to characterize synchronous system behavior. A logic state analyzer is a data domain monitoring instrument.
Digital System A system in which signals are digital; a system in which processes are accomplished with discrete, discontinuous data, frequently using parallel channels, lines, or nodes.
Display Qualifier See Clock Qualifier.
Display Window The sequence of system activity displayed by the monitoring instrument. In a logic analyzer, the window is defined by the trigger conditions plus any delay or indexing.
Don't Care A channel that may be in either state "0" or state "1".
Don't Care Triggering A triggering condition where all of the trigger bits are don't care. The first data that comes along will be traced.
Exclusive-OR A list display mode for some logic analyzers which display a logic 1 whenever two compared input states are different. See Halt.
External Trigger An active signal or an external logic analyzer input that will start (trigger) the analyzer.
Format Configuration of a logic analyzer, e.g., labels given to input channels, clock and logic polarities, and display presentation.
Formatted List Grouping the binary list to make it easier to read; e.g., a binary string may be subdivided into sets of four bits each, or these four bits may be presented as their hexadecimal equivalent.
Frequency Domain A domain that is represented by the amplitude of a signal on one axis and the frequency on the other axis. A spectrum analyzer is a frequency domain monitoring instrument.
Full-Duplex Serial system that includes separate paths for transmit and receive.
Fundamental Measurement With digital systems, the fundamental mea-

surements are the state-sequence and state-time. State-sequence is measured with a logic state analyzer while state-time is measured with a logic timing analyzer.

Glitch A narrow spike occurring in a digital system; an extraneous voltage pip in a signal.

Glitch Detectors Special circuits that detect a glitch.

Glitch Memory An auxiliary memory that stores the presence of any glitches between sample periods.

Glitch Triggering Triggering on a glitch on any specified channel. Usually combined with Boolean requirements on all lines.

Graph A plot of the equivalent weight of the state as a function of the state-sequence. A graph highlights order and flow of program activity.

Half-Duplex Serial system that has only one path for transmit and receive.

Halt Trigger mode on a logic analyzer that causes a continuous trace to stop under either $A = B$ or $A \neq B$ conditions, where A is the present state and B is a previous or defined trace stored in the analyzer.

Handshake A sequence of events that occur on control lines of a system to signal that data is available, data is being read, or that data has been read.

Hexadecimal A number represented to base 16. For numbers of decimal equivalence 10 through 15, the symbols A through F are used.

Hold Time The time following the active clock edge where the analyzer may sample data. Since many systems do not hold the data past the active edge, a logic analyzer should have a zero hold time.

HP-IB An interface bus developed by Hewlett-Packard for communication between instruments. Meets IEEE-488 standards.

Indexing Setting the number of samples or clock pulses to be skipped following the trigger word before a trace commences.

Instrumentation Bus See HP-IB.

Inverse Video A black on white display used to highlight trigger words; or in serial displays, the data received. In formatting an analyzer, it is used to indicate user-definable parameters.

Latch A glitch latch detects narrow pulses and stretches them such that they are traced by the clock.

List A logic analyzer display showing the state sequence of a digital system. See Trace.

Listener A device in a digital system that is reading data from the bus.

Logic Analyzer Instrument for monitoring data flow in the data domain. See Logic State Analyzer, Logic Timing Analyzer, and Serial Network Analyzer.

Logic Polarity Definition given to voltages with respect to the threshold. In positive logic, a voltage above the threshold is defined as a 1; in negative logic, the same voltage is defined as a 0.

Logic State Analyzer An instrument that monitors the state-sequences of a digital system.

Logic Timing Analyzer An instrument that monitors the activity of a digital system and presents its observations as a state-time display.

Map A plot of each state of a system—half of each word in the Y direction, the other half in the X direction. The map is often viewed in the continuous mode and is useful for observing the states in which activity is taking place.

Memory Depth The number of words that may be stored in memory.

Memory Roll Facility for rolling or shifting the logic analyzer display through the analyzer memory.

Memory Width The number of bits in each word sampled and stored in memory.

Microprocessor A central processing unit fabricated on one or two semiconductor chips. When joined with memory and I/O, the whole system may be referred to as a microcomputer.

Microprocessor Analyzer A special logic state analyzer that monitors microprocessor bus systems and displays the results in microprocessor mnemonics.

Mnemonic A set of symbols that combine a series of 0's and 1's as used by a machine into symbols that suggest the instruction to a human; e.g., LDA is load accumulator.

Monitoring Observation of the activity of a host system by a measurement instrument such as a logic analyzer. Ideally, such a monitoring instrument should be transparent to the host system.

Multiple Occurrences Part of the trigger conditions that require the analyzer to find the trigger state a specified number of times in order to completely satisfy the trigger conditions.

Multiplexed The process of transmitting more than one set of signals over one bus; e.g., address and data information could occur at different times on the one bus. What is on the bus would be defined by the control signals.

Negative Time Events that occur before the defined trigger conditions are satisfied are said to occur in negative time. See Pretrigger.

Nested Loop A subroutine enclosed within a larger routine.

NOT Trigger A trigger condition that initiates data acquisition any time a state other than the state specified occurs.

Nyquist Theorem Theorem states that two samples/cycle minimum are needed to characterize a band-limited signal (in practice five to ten are needed).

Octal Octal is a number represented to base 8.

Op Code The portion of a software instruction set that defines the next operation to be performed. Often extra information (the operand) will be required to define the data or location on which the op code will operate.

Operand The part of an instruction to a processor that defines the data or the location to which the op code refers.

Parity An extra bit in a data word that makes the whole word contain an even (or odd) number of bits of one polarity.
Pass Count See Multiple Occurrences.
Pattern Recognition Matching of the sample data with the preset trigger word.
Pattern Trigger Output Line See Trigger Output.
Polarity See Logic Polarity.
Posttrigger Posttrigger refers to the condition when the start of the trace is delayed (indexed) after the trigger word.
Pretrigger Number of words that will be displayed before the trigger word. It can never be greater than the memory capacity and is used in Trigger Ends Display configuration.
Probe The pod on the logic analyzer that actually connects to the circuit under test. Important criteria are probe loading and speed.
Processor The central processing unit of a computer or digital system. If fabricated on one or two chips, it could be termed a microprocessor.
Protocol The sequence of events or the format of signals or lines that must occur for the correct operation of a system.
Range Triggering Triggering over a range of values.
Resolution The time interval over which a transition displayed by a timing analyzer may have occurred. For a single channel this will be 1 clock period. Between channels, the resolution is ± 1 clock period.
RS-232C A serial data bus.
Sample Window The time about the sample instant when the analyzer registers data. The sample window consists of set-up and hold times.
Sampling Reading the voltage at discrete instances in time with the implied assumption that the waveform is constant until the next sample.
Selective Trace A trace where the data sampled is selectively edited before being stored in memory.
Sequence Restart Used with sequential trigger to restart the trigger sequence should a given state occur.
Sequential Trigger A trigger condition that must be satisfied by a series of states in the specified sequence.
Serial Analyzer See Serial Network Analyzer.
Serial Data Bus A bus on which the data is all transferred in a serial manner.
Serial Network Analyzer A logic analyzer designed to monitor (also synchronize and format) data on a serial bus.
Serial Synchronous Serial data or transmissions that include a clock.
Set-up Time The time prior to the active clock edge where data may be sampled by the analyzer.
Simulate To replace some equipment with an instrument that may be configured to operate as the original.

Skew The difference in the delays across channels between the probe tip and point when the data is interpreted by the analyzer.
Speed The clock rate at which data is acquired and stored in memory.
State The level of a signal with respect to a threshold level.
State Analyzer See Logic State Analyzer.
State Flow The sequence in which the various logic states occur.
Strobe See Sampling.
Sync A signal line that defines or synchronizes a reference point in a string of data.
Synchronous Analyzer Traces data in synchronism with the clock of the system under observation. See Logic State Analyzer.
Synchronous Data Data that coincides or is valid with a defined clock or control signal.
Table See List.
Talker A device in the system that is putting data onto the bus.
Threshold The signal level that divides one state from a second.
Threshold Adjust An adjustment control on a logic analyzer used to vary the voltage level that defines what a logic analyzer will interpret as a logic "0" or logic "1".
Threshold Range Spread of threshold voltage. With slow rise times it will limit resolution of timing analyzer.
Time Domain A domain that has as one axis an analog signal and as the other axis, time. An oscilloscope is a time domain monitoring instrument.
Time Duration Filter A circuit that ensures trigger conditions (i.e., Boolean combinations) are satisfied for a minimum time before actually triggering the analyzer.
Time Measurements Time measurements with logic analyzers that may be relative (between samples), absolute (from trigger word), or between trigger enable and disable.
Timing Analyzer See Logic Timing Analyzer.
Trace A set of readings of the state of a digital system; or a front panel control that tells a logic analyzer to start.
Trace Events Similar to trace triggers, except delay is added so that the Nth word past the trigger is traced.
Trace Triggers Only the trigger words are traced. See also Trace Events.
Transient Triggering Triggering of a timing analyzer on a state that only occurs as a transient.
Transparent Instrument An instrument that will not load or modify the performance of the system being monitored.
Trigger A word, or sequence of words or events, that defines the point where a logic analyzer references its trace to the system activity.
Trigger Disable A condition or state that cancels the trigger enable. See also Sequence Restart.

Trigger Enable A condition or state that must occur before the trigger word will be recognized. See also Arm.
Trigger Ends Trace The last word in the trace, less any indexing, is the trigger word. With this mode, indexing may be used to position the trigger word part way through the trace.
Trigger Output A signal out of a logic analyzer that signifies that trigger conditions are met. It may be used to synchronize external instruments such as oscilloscopes or to arm a second analyzer.
Trigger Qualifier An external signal that places additional constraints on satisfying trigger conditions; i.e., the analyzer is triggered only when the specified trigger state *and* the trigger qualifier conditions occur.
Trigger Starts Trace The first word in the trace (less indexing) is the trigger word.
Variable Threshold A facility that allows the threshold on a logic analyzer to be varied either for different digital families or to check marginal data transitions.

Index